Contents

Cars by Cars

Your quick reference guide to the 300 cars in the Guide

3

Every 12 months sees a crop of new cars enter the market place, but while there are years which pass by which raise just a small amount of interest, 1999 looks like being something special. There's the promise of some real excitement and glamour, with tantalising new models from Alfa Romeo, Jaguar, Maserati and a dozen others. But it is not just in the expensive category that things are looking up. Ford's Focus brings dramatic style into the family market, while Peugeot's sweet 206 delivers real panache to the supermini sector. For the enthusiast, 1999 is something to look forward to.

Alfa 166

Long-awaited replacement for the 164, the 166 will have to go some to make the same impact its predecessor did. The signs look promising - svelte styling and engines ranging from 140bhp to 226bhp.

BMW 3-Series

The mainstay of BMW's sales is replaced by a look-alike. Under the skin everything has been improved, with more space, classier interior and some new engines. Only saloons for now; coupes, estates and the rest at least a year away.

Audi TT

The concept car reached production reality late in 1998, and hungry buyers cannot wait to get their hands on this stunning coupe. Aggressive pricing has been possible by basing TT on the A3. In time a convertible version will follow.

BMW Z Coupe

The Z3 gains a roof and a touch more practicality - more luggage space but still seats for only two. Available only with the big engines - 2.8-litre, or 3.2-litre M-Power.

Chrysler 300M

Dramatic cab-forward styling could make this one of the most Euro-friendly cars to leaves the States. The huge interior and athletic performance add to the all-round appeal.

Cadillac Escalade

That Cadillac of all companies should build a 4x4 is a sign of the ever-increasing popularity of these vehicles in the States. The Escalade is based upon the Chevrolet Tahoe, but with luxurious leather and wood trimmings.

Chrysler Jeep Grand Cherokee

All-new for 1999, the Grand Cherokee looks even better than before. Built in both the States and Austria, it offers improved space coupled to a higher quality interior. Perhaps now it can seriously challenge the Range Rover.

Fiat Multipla

Fiat go oddball. The Multipla may well provide the answer to every family's needs. With six seats - three in front, three behind - the unusual interior is easily obscured by bizarre exterior. Still, change is a good thing.

Ford Focus

The dramatic styling of Ford's Escort-sized family car justifies a new name - and the continuation of the Escort alongside until the new model becomes accepted. Mondeo levels of interior space and much improved engines will help the appeal.

Chevrolet Corvette Hardtop

Lighter than the Coupe, and lacking the lift-out T-top panels, the Hardtop Corvette is the quickest - and least-expensive - of the new fifth - generation Vettes.

Lincoln LS

Lincoln is part of the giant Ford empire, and the LS is the American cousin of Jaguar forthcoming S-Type. Both use the same platform with common engines. The conservative Lincoln will be exported to Europe.

Mercedes Benz S-Class

Any car would look sleek after the outgoing S-Class, but the elegance of the replacement is sure to win it many new friends. Shorter, yet roomier inside, the S-Class is packed with advanced technical features.

Honda Capa

Honda's answer to the Mercedes-Benz A-Class, tall and complete with double floorpan for strength and stiffness.

Ford Cougar

This time Ford gets it right with its US-built coupe. Based on the Mondeo, but re-engineered to give a far more sporting drive, the Cougar does the business on both the turns and the drive-way.

Kia Credos

Troubled Kia enters the mainstream family market. The Credos seems to have been produced a hundred times before by second-tier far eastern manufacturers, a recipe which may work at home but will hardly encourage exports.

Honda Accord

With three versions of the Accord for different continents, this is the new UK-built saloon for Europe. As ever it has an impressive engineering package, but it looks like Honda is getting closer with the exterior design too.

Maserati Coupe

Much-needed replacement for the Ghibli, the Maserati Coupe is the first new car since the take-over of the company by Ferrari. The twin-turbo V8 will be familiar, but style is refreshingly new. Hopefully, so will be the quality.

Mazda 323

All-new for 1999, the styling of Mazda's smaller family car is far less dramatic than before, but much more practical. The five-door hatchback remains the strength of the range; revised engines help the economy.

Mitsubishi Space Runner and Wagon

The Space Wagon was one of the original MPVs, while the Runner foresaw the Renault Scenic by a good five years. The replacements offer more power and improved packaging.

Jaguar S-Type

A Jaguar becomes more affordable with the new S-Type. Smaller than the current XJ-range, and designed to compete with cars the size of BMW's 5-Series, this is a computer rendition of the car that is sure to massively increase Jaguar's popularity.

Mitsubishi Space Star

It may look like a small MPV, but the Space Star is more of a hatchback with a wide, high but short design. This one is built in Europe. But does Mitsubishi really need four Space vehicles in its armoury?

Lexus IS200

Lexus enters BMW 3-Series territory. Straight-six 2.0-litre power unit, six-speed manual transmission, rear wheel drive, huge wheels and sharp interior - the basics look spot on.

Peugeot 206

Peugeot's new supermini slips into a gap between the 106 and 306. Spiritual successor to the much-loved 205, the 206 has the style and mechanical package to enthral a new generation of drivers.

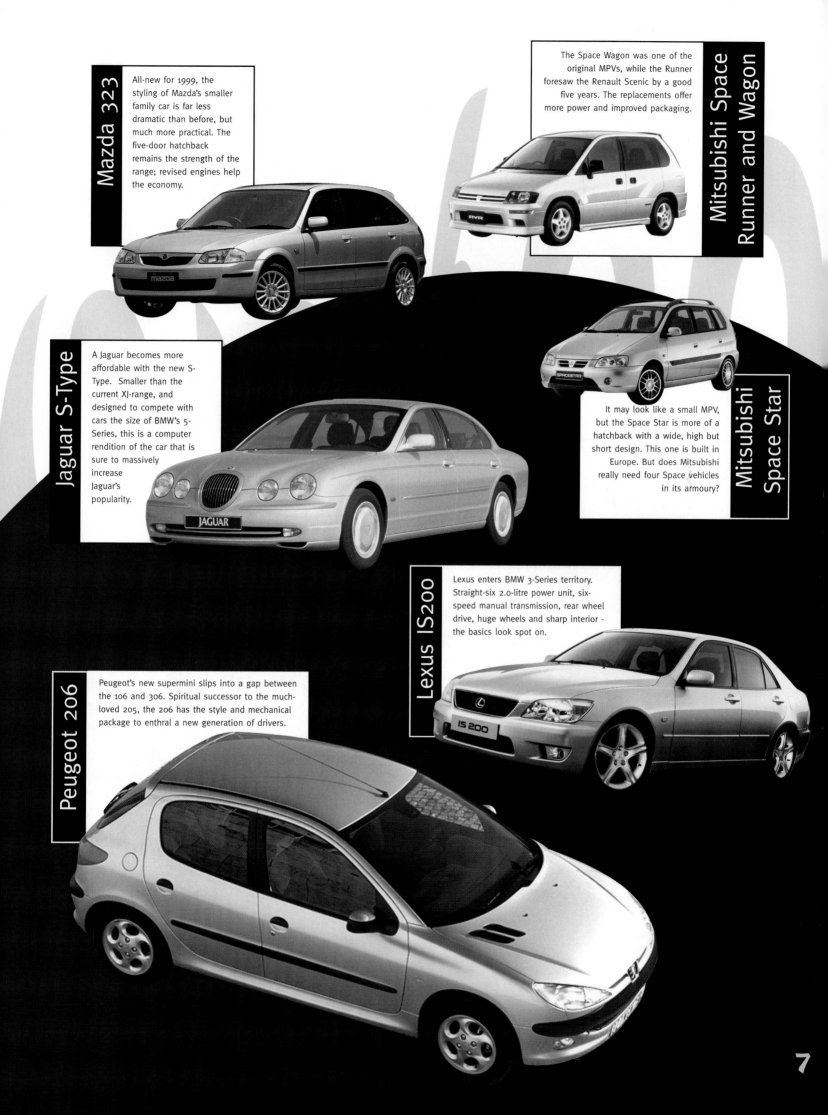

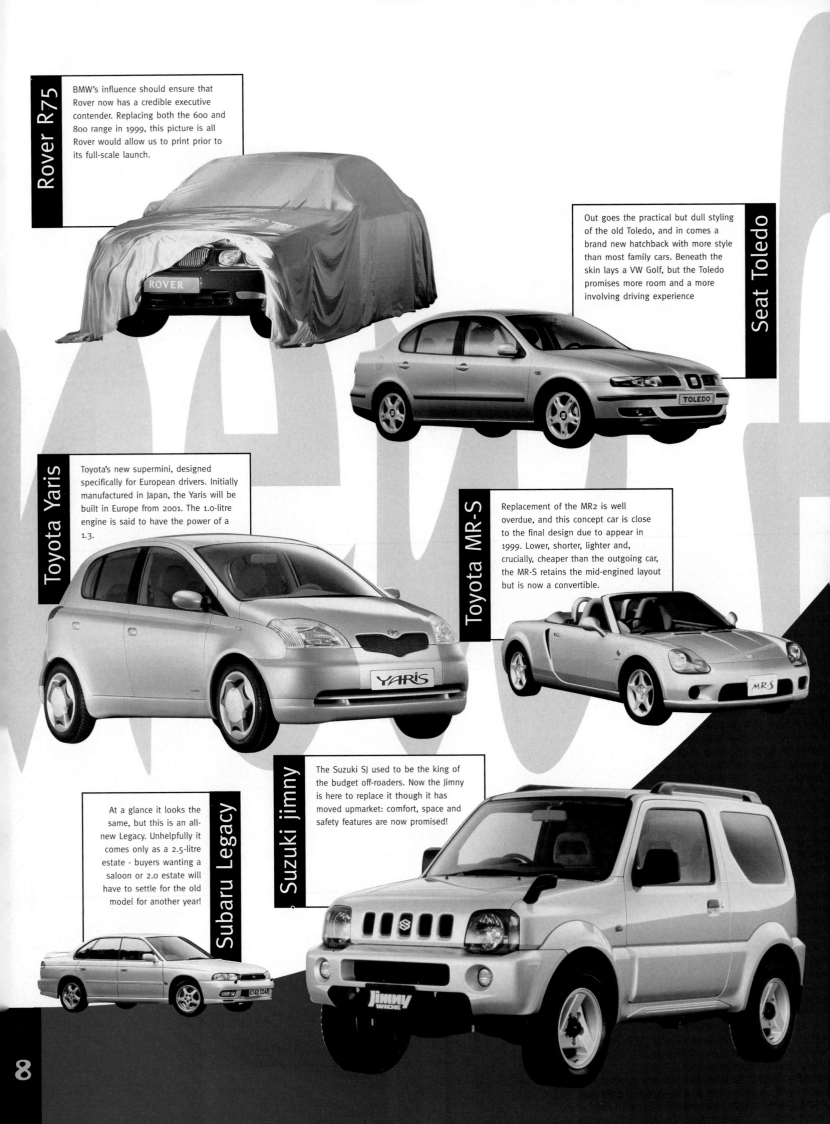

Rover R75

BMW's influence should ensure that Rover now has a credible executive contender. Replacing both the 600 and 800 range in 1999, this picture is all Rover would allow us to print prior to its full-scale launch.

Seat Toledo

Out goes the practical but dull styling of the old Toledo, and in comes a brand new hatchback with more style than most family cars. Beneath the skin lays a VW Golf, but the Toledo promises more room and a more involving driving experience

Toyota Yaris

Toyota's new supermini, designed specifically for European drivers. Initially manufactured in Japan, the Yaris will be built in Europe from 2001. The 1.0-litre engine is said to have the power of a 1.3.

Toyota MR-S

Replacement of the MR2 is well overdue, and this concept car is close to the final design due to appear in 1999. Lower, shorter, lighter and, crucially, cheaper than the outgoing car, the MR-S retains the mid-engined layout but is now a convertible.

Suzuki jimny

The Suzuki SJ used to be the king of the budget off-roaders. Now the Jimny is here to replace it though it has moved upmarket: comfort, space and safety features are now promised!

Subaru Legacy

At a glance it looks the same, but this is an all-new Legacy. Unhelpfully it comes only as a 2.5-litre estate - buyers wanting a saloon or 2.0 estate will have to settle for the old model for another year!

Vauxhall/Opel Zafira

Renault showed that there was a big market for a multi-purpose vehicle smaller than the Espace, and within a year many more will have followed. The Zafira is Astra based, with the advantage over the Scenic of offering seven seats.

TVR Speed 12

Increasingly ambitious TVR has topped everything it has done before. The Speed Twelve boasts over 600 bhp from its 7.7-litre V12 engine - the ambition is to go faster that the McLaren F1 at a quarter of the cost - £150,000.

Volkswagen Lupo

As small cars get bigger, there eventually comes a need to slot in a new small car at the bottom fill the void. The jolly-looking Lupo is Volkswagen's sub-Polo car, designed to compete with the Ford Ka.

Volvo S80

Volvo gets modern with its new flagship - and some would say about time too. While billed as the world's safest car it also has all the accomplishment of its German rivals, plus performance aplenty.

Volkswagen Bora

VW's Golf-derived saloons have at best achieved mixed sales success. This time the recipe is different. Out goes boring practicality, in comes a heavy redesign of the hatchback aimed at buyers of sports saloons.

Volkswagen Beetle

It is already a rip-roaring success, with the order books filled for a year in every country it goes on sale. But while it may have the look of the original, the new Beetle is a far more accomplished, far more expensive, package.

Picking the right car from the 250 models on offer in the UK is never going to be easy. Many buyers just go with the flow, choosing a car from one of the major manufacturers. That is rarely a completely bad idea, but blinkered decision making does mean that missing out on some gems that aren't necessarily one of the big sellers. Here we look at which cars top the sales charts, and pick our favourite.

the top ten

Key: Longer bars = more sales

1. Ford Escort

62,200

2. Ford Fiesta

61,900

3. Ford Mondeo

53,700

4. Vauxhall Vectra

50,000

5. Renault Megane

45,400

6. Vauxhall Corsa

37,700

7. Peugeot 306

37,300

res: JATO

Budget Buys

A tight budget used to mean resorting to the second-hand market or a poor-quality East-European produced model. Now the big boys are thinking small, and are making fine quality cars in miniature, with price tags to match. The Ford Ka, for one, has taken the sector by storm. Using the Fiesta as its base ensures it drives well and is cheap to run, but its funky looks are the real attraction. Skoda's Felicia range appeals to no-nonsense family car buyers who can see past the badge to the fine-quality car you would expect the Volkswagen Group. The Fiat Seicento is a reworking of the popular Cinquecento with better quality, refinement and safety, though it does seem some rivals are now able to beat Fiat in its traditional area of expertise.

Editor's choice: Skoda Felicia

1. Ford Ka
2. Skoda Felicia
3. Seat Arosa
4. Fiat Seicento
5. Suzuki Swift

Superminis

Even if the Fiesta was awful to drive, the might of Ford's blue oval badge would make sure it still sold thousands. Luckily, the latest Fiesta is a real cracker, with big-car refinement and wonderful handling. The 16-valve engines give it a sporty feel and ensure running costs are kept low - only the limited room and a relatively high price spoil the package. VW's Polo scores with plenty of interior space and the same big car feel. Great resale values and a long warranty have made it seriously desirable. Vauxhall's Corsa is spacious and good-looking, but its overall refinement is way behind the class leaders. Renault's new Clio is uninspired but appeals with great value and equipment, while Peugeot's 106 is fun to drive.

Editor's choice: Volkswagen Polo

1. Ford Fiesta
2. Vauxhall Corsa
3. Peugeot 106
4. Renault Clio
5. Fiat Punto

Small Family Cars

Sensibly-sized and priced to fit most pockets, the small family car sector is the biggest and most competitive in the UK. It has been an exciting year with the arrival of the new Vauxhall Astra and Volkswagen Golf, but despite this, Ford's ageing Escort continues to be the best seller. The spacious Astra is fine to drive but has so far failed to capture the imagination of family car buyers - unlike the new VW Golf, which suffers from restricted supply. The Renault Megane is one of the best selling French cars ever, thanks to an extensive range which encompasses a wide range of models. The British-built Peugeot 306 is a fine driver's car - even with the small-engined and diesel versions - but it's the GTI-6 and convertible really turn heads.

Editor's choice: Vauxhall Astra

1. Ford Escort
2. Renault Megane
3. Peugeot 306
4. Vauxhall Astra
5. Rover 200

Medium Family Cars

The staple diet of family and fleet drivers, the medium-sized car can now rival the prestige brands for quality and driving ability. Ford dominates the sector and the Mondeo is good to drive and easy to live with, thanks to a well-thought out interior and strong engine range. The Vectra seems lacklustre in comparison, especially inside, but a wide choice and the Vauxhall badge ensure it is still a top seller. Rover still retains a place in the charts despite the 400's high price and smaller dimensions. Peugeot's 406 adds a bit of glamour to the sector, but the lack of a hatchback model slows down sales. It is the VW Passat which is causing a real stir though, despite its limited supply.

Editor's choice: Volkswagen Passat

1. Ford Mondeo
2. Vauxhall Vectra
3. Rover 400
4. Peugeot 406
5. Renault Laguna

Compact Executive Cars

While buyers may hanker after a large luxury car with a prestige badge, most will have to make do with the cheapest model in the range. The car which moulded this sector, BMW's 3-Series, continues to top the sales charts, with a new model to see off the competition for another few years. The Audi A4 is the only car which has ever come close to toppling the BMW. Great looks, quality and fine performance mean the car has re-established the Audi brand in the UK. Mercedes' C-Class has all the attributes you would expect from the marque, but prices and equipment levels limit its popularity. Expect to see the Alfa's great 156 breaking up the German's domination of the market before long.

Editor's choice: Alfa Romeo 156

1. BMW 3-Series
2. Audi A4
3. Mercedes C-Class
4. Rover 600
5. Volvo s/V70

Executive Cars

With the demise of the Ford Scorpio, Vauxhall's Omega has been left as the only choice for many UK company directors. It's surprisingly good to drive, but buyers have to do without the all-important prestige badge. The BMW 5-Series is the car rivals have failed to beat in this sector. Refinement is exceptional, but the Five is reasonably equipped and great fun to drive. The Mercedes E-Class traditionally appeals more to the more mature motorist, who appreciates its safety and quality. The Audi A6 may not be a match for the BMW, but keen prices, adventurous styling and a huge interior mean it sells well. The understated but excellent Saab 9-5 is the best car from the Swedish manufacturer in years.

Editor's choice: BMW 5-Series

1. Vauxhall Omega
2. BMW 5-Series
3. Mercedes E-Class
4. Audi A-6
5. Saab 9-5

Sports Cars

With a roadster renaissance in full swing, the MGF was almost guaranteed success because of its heritage. The mid-mounted engine ensures it handles superbly, but unfortunately, it means there is little luggage space and reliability is not the best either. BMW's Z3 appeals with stunning looks and traditional BMW quality. The handling isn't as exciting as more sporting rivals, but the Z3 is a drop-top without the compromises. The Mazda MX5 is the car which renewed the interest in roadsters world-wide, and the new model's improvements keep the car fresh without diluting its appeal. Mercedes SLK and the Porsche Boxster would sell more but demand is running way ahead of supply.

Editor's choice: Mazda MX-5

1. MGF
2. BMW Z3
3. Mazda MX-5
4. Mercedes SLK
5. Porsche Boxster

Coupes

Buying a coupe makes a statement about your lifestyle, so it's no surprise that the BMW 3-Series is still the car to be seen in. It is less practical and more expensive than the saloon, but it looks good and drives well. A replacement is imminent and will strengthen its position. The head-turning Ford Puma is in a different class with fine engines and a bargain price and appealing to the sort of buyers who used to aspire to a hot hatch. The Hyundai Coupe is another bargain priced stunner which has lifted the image of the Korean brand immeasurably. Mercedes CLK owners are feeling smug - demand is so high that anyone placing an order now is unlikely to see their car until the millennium.

Editor's choice: Ford Puma

1. BMW 3-Series
2. Ford Puma
3. Vauxhall Tigra
4. Hyundai Coupe
5. Mercedes-Benz CLK

Luxury Cars

The luxury car sector may only represent a tiny number of sales, but we can be proud that British cars can still take on the best and win. The Jaguar XJ saloon has a new range of V8 engines with improved economy and performance. The price is still competitive and only the cramped interior lets it down. The Range Rover is still the choice for those who demand luxury and off-road ability. It may be thirsty and expensive, but the off-roader's practicality and road-presence ensure success. Mercedes' S-Class is about to be replaced by a smaller and more fuel efficient model which will closely rival the excellent BMW 7-Series. The Lexus is arguably the most refined car in the world.

Editor's choice: Jaguar XJ8

1. **Jaguar XJ8**
2. **Range Rover**
3. **BMW 7-Series**
4. **Mercedes S-Class**
5. **Lexus LS400**

Exotics

Having an exotic car should be all about turning heads and exciting yourself with race-car performance and handling. Jaguar has taken the market by storm with its XK8. The beautiful styling makes cars twice the price look dull, while the interior is a combination of traditional wood and leather luxury and the latest in technology. The new Porsche 911 may not be as involving to drive as the legendary model it replaced, but it is just as quick and is also more refined, practical and safer. Mercedes' SL may be looking and feeling old, but new engines have made it more competitive. Ferraris are the stuff of schoolboy dreams, and the 355 doesn't let down those who can finally afford one.

Editor's choice: Jaguar XK8

1. **Jaguar XK8**
2. **Porsche 911**
3. **Mercedes SL**
4. **Ferrari**
5. **BMW 8-Series**

MPV's

It's not just families who appreciate the versatility offered by an MPV. The latest cars are more than vans with windows and everyone from businessmen to mountain bikers can appreciate their adaptability. Almost all of the big manufacturers now offer multi-seater models, but it is Ford which takes most sales with its Galaxy although it is virtually identical to the VW Sharan and Seat Alhambra. The Chrysler Voyager has impressed buyers with its space, equipment and value but it is too big for most British buyers and the engine range is too limited. The latest version of Renault's Espace is innovative inside but has moved upmarket and now has to be content with lower sales.

Editor's choice: Ford Galaxy

1. **Ford Galaxy**
2. **VW Sharan**
3. **Chrysler Voyager**
4. **Renault Espace**
5. **Seat Alhambra**

Off-Roaders

Owning a 4x4 seems foolish unless you often need to go off-road, with high prices, extra fuel consumption and flawed road manners a few of the many drawbacks. But buyers continue to be drawn by the lifestyle image and high driving position. The more fashionable off-roaders are the big sellers, with Honda's CR-V and the Toyota RAV4 thriving thanks to car-like driving experiences. But Land-Rover can do little wrong. Its new Freelander has the looks to succeed as well as excellent on and off-road manners. The Discovery is more of a real mud-plugger, with awesome ability off road. A new model, due soon, will see it move upmarket.

Editor's choice: Land Rover Freelander

1. **Land Rover Freelander**
2. **Land Rover Discovery**
3. **Honda CR-V**
4. **Toyota RAV4**
5. **Vauxhall Frontera**

Nowhere will you find a more comprehensive guide to the world's cars. Now with nearly 40 per cent more space devoted to the catalogue section of the 1999 edition, we bring you the details on 300 of the most popular vehicles money can buy.

Since the 1998 edition we have driven hundreds of new cars, interviewed dozens of car company directors and interrogated a similar number of design and development engineers. It has given us the background and authority to pronounce on all the new cars that have come to market as well as giving us the inside information on what is to come.

One of the major developments in this year's World Car Guide is the section on each manufacturer. It gives the low-down on what each car makers is all about, and looks into how the company may develop in the future. The Guide also contains many more pictures than before, highlighting the wide diversity of body style that can be offered under one model name.

As always, each car entry gives you details of the range plus the model which exhibits the best all-round characteristics. While it would have been all too easy to pick the most expensive version of each car, cost has been included in the equation too, so that our Best All-Rounder represents a fine blend between its qualities as a car and its value for money.

The country of manufacturer becomes an increasingly thorny issue. Is a Ford Fiesta a "British" car? It may be but there is a 50:50 chance that it has been built in Spain. How about the BMW Z3 - German? No, it comes from the USA. Toyota Avensis - Japanese? Wrong again, it is built in Britain. But even "built" is confusing, for what the manufacturer usually means that is where the final assembly takes place. The new Peugeot 206 is built in France and England, but the British models use imported body panels, engines, gearboxes and suspension. Does it all matter? Probably not, because all manufacturers make doubly sure the new factories they build produce cars to the same or even better standards than the original.

Car entries in the catalogue contain a limited amount of technical data, but for a fuller account, a comprehensive database is included after the main catalogue section. It contains information on almost every model listed in the main catalogue section, although occasionally data on the newest cars was not available before we went to press.

Finally a comprehensive listing of new car prices for the UK is presented. This section went to press at the last possible minute to ensure it is as up-to-date as possible. However, car prices change on a regular basis, so for the latest up-to-the-minute details look in the weekly Auto Express, which contains the most accurate new car prices in the UK.

Picking the right car

Cars have usually fallen into a number of convenient categories, an idea supported by the industry which has been keen to develop new cars that compete with existing models, rather than going out on a limb. So the new Ford Focus will be much the same size as the Escort, even though, as things always go, it will be a touch longer and roomier, a bit quicker and marginally more economical.

Occasionally car manufacturers are prepared to step out of line. Renault did it very successfully with the Megane Scenic. So has Mercedes-Benz with the A-Class, although that car's long term staying power has yet to be proven.

These are highly individual cars. At the other extreme a fascinating blend of mechanical components can be used to produce several cars from the same basic ingredients. The Volkswagen Group is a master of this. Take one floorpan, add a set of engines, transmissions and suspensions, then design a range of distinctive body styles. The result is the Volkswagen Golf, VW Beetle, Audi A3, Audi TT, Skoda Octavia and Seat Toledo. Or simpler still, take the same vehicle and just stick a different badge on it - what you get is the Citroen Synergie, Peugeot 806, Fiat Ulysse and Lancia Z. Economic realities mean that this type of deals can only increase. Below are listed the most significant on the market today.

SMALL CARS

Ford Fiesta and Mazda 121

Mazda's 121 is identical to the Ford Fiesta, built on the same production line in Dagenham. But despite a far better warranty on the 121, the Fiesta outsells it a hundred times in the UK.

Peugeot 106 and Citroen Saxo

Peugeot facelifted the 106 for 1997 with a new nose, tail and interior. Citroen adopted the car at the same time with only subtle changes to the exterior, plus a different dashboard.

Suzuki Swift and Subaru Justy

In earlier incarnations there was a geniune Subaru Justy. Now it is merely a four-wheel-drive version of Suzuki's Swift. Both are built in Hungary.

Seat Arosa and Volkswagen Lupo

Volkswagen's just-launched Lupo may look distinctly charming, but it has been around for well over a year wearing the clothes of the Seat Arosa.

Volkswagen Polo, Seat Ibiza and Seat Cordoba

VW owns Seat, and all these small cars are similar under the skin. The Polo saloon and Estate use the Cordoba body with very few changes.

FAMILY CARS

Audi A3, Seat Toledo, Skoda Octavia, Volkswagen Golf, Volkswagen Beetle

This one is cleverer than most, because the Octavia and new Toledo have been made to look like they are a class bigger than the Golf and Audi, while the Beetle is different again. Oh, and the TT coupe is also based on the same chassis.

Rover 400 and Honda Civic

Originally a Honda design, Rover restyled it and inserted its own engines. In 1997 Honda had a make-over on its five-door Civic so the two cars look increasingly different. Both cars are manufactured in the UK. Confusingly, three-door and saloon Civics are of a different generation.

Volvo V40 and Mitsubishi Carisma

Built in same factory in Holland, with the same underpinnings, but distinctly different bodies and engines. About as different as you can get with a jointly developed car.

MPVs OR PEOPLE CARRIERS

Citroen Evasion, Citroen Synergy, Peugeot 806, Fiat Ulysse, Lancia Z

A joint venture between the French PSA company (Citroen and Peugeot) and Italian Fiat (Fiat and Lancia). Same engines in all, differences in trim.

Ford Galaxy, Volkswagen Sharan and Seat Alhambra

Built in a Portuguese factory. Turbo-diesel and V6 engines from VW, but each company uses its own 2.0-litre.

OFF-ROADERS

Isuzu Trooper and Vauxhall/Opel Monterey

Sold for several years in the UK by Isuzu and in Europe by Opel, before Vauxhall muscled in during 1994. Vauxhall sales have been poor, and the Monterey may be dropped in the UK

Isuzu Rodeo and Vauxhall/Opel Frontera

The Japanese-manufactured Rodeo is little seen in Europe, but it is also built in England and sold as the Frontera throughout the European Community.

AC

AC has a long and chequered history as a car manufacturer - a company that went from building one of the most dramatic sports cars in history to making ugly reinforced plastic cars for disabled drivers in order to keep its head above water. Today's business is based in Surrey, England, and concentrates once more on that most charismatic of cars, the Cobra. Or that is what most people know it as, for continued arguments about who owns that name means the car has variously been called the AC Mark IV or, as now, the Superblower. It's a real blood-and-guts sports car, but the AC Ace hovers precariously in the background as a more luxurious high performance offering.

Ace

AC Ace

It may have the classic AC badge on its nose, but the latest Ace is supposed to be a thoroughly modern rival to the Mercedes SL and Jaguar XK8. On paper it seems impressive too, with an US-sourced 5.0-litre V8 delivering supercar performance, but AC's limited resources mean the design is too dated and flawed.

The Ace is now available with the choice of hard and soft tops - Mercedes SL style - but its style and quality is unlikely to tempt many Merc buyers. The interior is beautifully trimmed in traditional wood and leather but mass-produced Ford switchgear spoils the effect and makes it a brave choice for £75,000.

Body styles Coupe **Engine capacity** 5.0V8 **Price from** £75,000 **Manufactured in** England

Superblower

The roads may be awash with look-alike kit-cars, but the Superblower is the only Cobra which can wear the AC badge with pride - and legally. The latest incarnation of the sixties supercar classic aims to thrill with a huge supercharged V8 engine producing an awesome 355bhp.

The price of a Superblower - £70,000 - will buy some very competent sports cars, and almost all of them will be more comfortable, practical and safer than the AC. The brutish straight-line performance, old-fashioned handling and famous name may be enough to part some enthusiasts from their money, but most just wish it would die gracefully.

Body styles Convertible
Engine capacity 5.0V8 Supercharged
Price from £70,000
Manufactured in England

alfa romeo

Alfa Romeo

Charisma and brio remain cornerstones of the appeal of an Alfa Romeo though the demands of mainstream buyers means that they have become less eccentric than in the past. The 156 Car of the Year shows just how far the company can go without losing that appeal. This has been followed by the new large car, the 166, launched in Paris in Autumn 1998, with right-hand-drive cars due early in 1999. Also for 1999 are revised versions of the GTV and Spider, with engines from the 156/166, plus an impressive 2.5-litre turbo-diesel for the saloons.

Alfa Romeo 166   *new!*

The new 166 combines, Alfa Romeo hopes, the prestige, comfort and performance of a luxury saloon with that typical Alfa flair. Based upon a development of the Lancia Kappa floorpan, the 166 is, like all new cars of this class, brimming with technology, but in the end it will be the driving experience that makes or breaks it.

The potential looks promising particularly after the excellent achievement with the 156. The engines are familiarly powerful: 2.0-litre, a 2.0-litre turbo V6 with 205bhp (mainly for the Italian market), a 190bhp 2.5V6 and 226bhp 3.0V6. There also a common-rail 2.5-litre, five-cylinder turbo-diesel, which may make its way into the UK.

Best All-Rounder: Too early to tell

Body styles Saloon
Engine capacity 2.0, 2.0 Turbo, 2.5V6, 3.0V6, 2.5TD
Price from £25,000
Manufactured in Italy

Alfa Romeo 145/146

Alfa has never been a company for doing things the conventional way, so it split its Escort-sized cars into two separate models. The 145 is the boxy-styled three-door, while the 146 the fastback five- door. Both share the same chassis and engine, and are as interesting to to drive as they are to look at.

New twin spark engines inject a little verve to both ranges, adding a distinctive sporty zing to the driving experience. Even the 1.6-litre is good fun to drive, but the 150bhp 2.0-litre models are among the hottest hot-hatches around. The ride, handling and comfort levels are not up with the best in the class though.

Best All-Rounder: 146 1.8 Twin Spark

Body styles
Hatchback

Engine capacity
1.6, 1.8, 2.0

Price from
£14,500

Manufactured in
Italy

Alfa Romeo 156

That the 156 could have won Car of the Year on its looks alone is to seriously underplay its virtues. Beneath that stylish exterior and the classiest interior Alfa has ever managed, lies a great sports saloon. Choose from 1.8 to 2.5 V6 engines, any of which gives a spirited performance. There are also a couple of turbo-diesels for some markets.

The driving position isn't great but the seats are comfortable and room is only a problem for taller back passengers. The boot is spacious too. With the confidence that Alfas are becoming better built, owning a 156 should be just as pleasurable as driving one.

Best All-Rounder: 156 2.0 Twin Spark

Body styles
Saloon

Engine capacity
1.8, 2.0, 2.5V6, 1.9TD, 2.5TD

Price from
£18,000

Manufactured in
Italy

Alfa Romeo GTV

Cars don't get much more dramatic looking than the GTV. Designed and built by Italian styling house Pininfarina, the Italian coupe goes almost as well as it looks. The front wheel drive chassis won't appeal to sportscar fans, but the great handling and fabulous engines will.

The 150bhp 2.0-litre Twin Spark is eager to please, but it can't deliver the speed to match those supercar looks. The new 24-valve 3.0-litre V6 engined version is pricey but finally delivers the performance the excellent chassis has been crying out for. At last a real alternative to a BMW coupe.

Best All-Rounder: GTV 3.0 V6 24v

Body styles
Coupe

Engine capacity
2.0, 3.0V6

Price from
£22,000

Manufactured in
Italy

Alfa Romeo Spider

Taking the roof off a GTV should be a recipe for fun, and the topless Alfa certainly has the looks to live up to the classic heritage of the Spider name. However in practice it doesn't really gel, and is more of a cruiser than a sportscar, with excessive body shake, fiddly hood and a poor driving position.

There is only one engine option with the Spider - it's the 2-litre Twin Spark or nothing. The 150bhp unit struggles with the car's weight, and it looks pricey next to similarly powered roadster rivals, but most buyers sacrifice all for those looks. The Lusso pack is a worthwhile option, adding air con and leather.

Pick of the range: Lusso

Body styles
Convertible

Engine capacity
2.0

Price from
£23,300

Manufactured in
Italy

Aston Martin

Hand-built by craftsman in Newport Pagnell, England has long been the calling card of Aston Martin ownership and it remains true that if you buy one of the classic lines - the V8, Volante, or Vantage - that is just what you get. But these models cost £150,000-plus and sales of cars at these stratospheric prices are pitifully small, even on a world-wide scenario. So, under Ford ownership, the DB7 makes up the majority of Aston Martins sold - it's cheaper and built from components brought in from outside contractors on a production line 40 miles away.

DB7 Volante

V8 Volante

Aston Martin DB7

When the base model of the range costs £85,000, you know you are looking at a classy manufacturer. And they don't come much more prestigious than Aston. The gorgeous DB7 uses mainly Jaguar components, including the supercharged straight-six engine, but the craftsman built wood and leather interior and kudos of the badge make it worth the extra.

The coupe DB7 is a grand tourer of the old school, with ultra refinement and mile munching ability, but it is still capable of surprising supercars with its 165mph performance and supercharger-boosted mid-range punch. The Volante convertible is more of a cruiser, but open-top cars don't come much more desirable.

Body styles Coupe, Convertible **Engine capacity** 3.2 Supercharged **Price from** £85,000
Manufactured in England

V8-Vantage

Even the cheapest V8 Coupe costs more than most people's mortgages, but for most Aston Martin enthusiasts the V8 and Vantage are the real thing. Handbuilt by craftsmen using skills almost extinct elsewhere in the industry, cars are made exactly to the customer's specification, down to the colour of the seat piping.

It may have the luxury and built quality to match - or even better - a Rolls Royce, but each of these cars is capable of scaring most drivers with a truck-sized 5.3-litre V8. The V8 Volante is an open-top gentleman's club on wheels, but the awesome tuned 550bhp Vantage is one of the fastest and exclusive cars in the world.

Body styles
Coupe, Convertible
Engine capacity 5.3 V8, 5.3 Twin Turbo
Price from £150,000
Manufactured in England

audi

Audi

Stuck in something of a grey area even five years ago, offering neither the thrill of a BMW nor the prestige of a Mercedes-Benz, Audi has turned itself around to rival the desirability of both its German competitors. Much can be put down to the success of the A4, which has led to better things in other models. The A6 is now one of the strongest cars in its class, while the technological prowess of the aluminium A8 and stunning new TT put the company in great stead.

Audi TT   *new!*

When it made its first appearance as a concept car, few thought the stunning TT coupe and roadster would make it into production. But Audi is feeling brave, and the production car, on sale in the UK from next spring, looks almost identical inside and out to the wild show car.

The TT gets two engine options, both 1.8-litres and both turbo-charged to produce 180bhp or 225bhp. Quattro four-wheel drive is compulsory on the more powerful model, with front wheel drive an option on the 180. The result is a breathtaking sports car, with dynamic or just plain explosive acceleration, depending upon your choice of engine, and leach-like roadholding. You have to drive around some transmission jerk in the quattro, but otherwise there's little to fault in the TT.

Body styles: Coupe, convertible
Engine capacity: 1.8 Turbo
Price from: £25,000
Manufactured in: Hungary

Audi A3

It may be the same underneath as the new Volkswagen Golf, but the smallest Audi still exudes the sort of quality and style which lifts it into a higher class. It needs to though, as it's pricey for a hatchback of this size, and only available with three doors.

The range starts with fine 1.6-litre and 1.8-litre petrol engines, but it is the 150bhp turbo which will get the enthusiasts excited. Oddly the 110bhp turbo-diesel is the real star of the range with 45mpg economy and real GTi style performance. The SE package adds equipment without a bank-breaking dip into the options list.

Best All-Rounder: A3 1.9 TDI SE

Body styles
Hatchback

Engine capacity
1.6, 1.8, 1.8 Turbo, 1.9TDi

Price from
£14,200

Manufactured in
Germany

Audi A4

The only car to have ever challenged the dominance of the BMW 3-Series in the compact executive market with fine handling and refinement blended with top quality, style and comfort. The Avant is more of a lifestyle estate than a load lugger while the four-wheel-drive quattro models offer unrivalled roadholding in this class.

The A4 range is now even stronger with the arrival of a smooth and responsive 2.4-litre V6 petrol and torquey 150bhp V6 diesel. Entry-level 1.6-litre models feel underpowered, and quattro is only available with turbo-diesel and 2.8-litre petrol engines. The high-performance S4 arrived in the autumn of 1998.

Best All-Rounder: A4 2.4SE

Body styles
Saloon, Estate

Engine capacity
1.6, 1.8, 1.8 Turbo, 2.4V6, 2.8V6, 2.7V6 Turbo, 1.9TDi, 2.5TDi

Price from
£17,000

Manufactured in
Germany

Audi A6

The A6 is Audi's seriously viable alternative to the BMW 5-Series and, like BMW, is available in saloon or estate forms. The bold, fashionably-styled body houses a variety of refined engines ranging from a 1.8-litre Turbo through to a 2.8-litre V6, and includes two punchy turbo-diesels.

Inside, the cabin is faultlessly designed and screwed together, the cockpit's ambience clinical but impressive. Accommodation front and rear is excellent too and there's ample luggage space in both body styles. Refinement is good, even though the ride quality can be a little firm, a compromise to ensure taut handling. The A6 is a fine car indeed.

Best All-Rounder: A6 2.5 V6 TDi

Body styles
Saloon, Estate

Engine capacity
1.8 Turbo, 2.4V6, 2.8V6, 1.9TDi, 2.5TDi

Price from
£23,800

Manufactured in
Germany

Audi A8

Audi's BMW 7-Series rivalling flagship is not just pretty to look at, but is a real technological tour-de-force thanks to its all-aluminium spaceframe bodyshell. Keeping the weight down means economy and performance are class-topping, with discreet looks not as ostentatious as rivals from Mercedes and BMW.

The 2.8-litre V6 feels sluggish but the V8s are real refined flyers, especially with the roadholding advantages of Audi's quattro four-wheel drive. The S8 is a real supercar chaser in terms of performance, despite its size and amazing opulence. Looks pricey next to Jaguar's finest, but the A8 is a much underrated luxury alternative.

Best All-Rounder: A8 4.2 quattro

Body styles	Price from
Saloon	£36,600

Engine capacity	Manufactured in
2.8V6, 3.7V8, 4.2V8, 2.5TDi	Germany

Audi Cabriolet

Like many competitors, Audi bases its Cabriolet on a superseded car, in this case the 80 saloon. But some judicious development has kept it up with the game, and though the inside is much like the old 80, like the exterior, it hasn't dated too much. The slab-like dashboard is functional and solid, with a quality feel which puts many new prestige cars to shame.

The driving experience is more cruiser than sports car, with steering that lacks enough feel for the enthusiastic driver. But if a head turning, relaxed cruise is your bag, then the Cabriolet still competes.

Best All-Rounder: Cabriolet 2.6

Body styles	Price from
Convertible	£23,300

Engine capacity	Manufactured in
1.8, 2.4V6, 2.8V6	Germany

Bentley

1998 has been a year of great turmoil at the UK's oldest independent car maker. After such a great start with the launch of the new Arnage saloon, things became increasingly confusing with the sale of the company. Finally Volkswagen ended up the victor. It will split off Bentley from Rolls Royce and will soon have to replace the BMW twin-turbo V8 engine in the Arnage with a power unit of its own. It will be a time yet before the dust settles.

Azure

Bentley Arnage   *new!*

The Arnage is Bentley's all-new car that moves the boundaries far away from the outgoing saloon. With technical input from BMW, including the 4.4-litre twin-turbocharged V8, five-speed automatic transmission and computer-controlled suspension, braking and stability control systems, there is much to be proud of.

The resulting performance is ultra-refined but breathtakingly effective. The clever suspension ensures that while the ride comfort remains as good as ever, the handling is on a new sporting plane. None of this is at the exclusion of sumptuous luxury, of course. The Bentley is as good as the Rolls in this respect.

Azure Convertible

Body styles Saloon **Engine capacity** 4.4V8 Twin Turbo **Price from** £145,000 **Manufactured in** England

Bentley Azure

For those who disdain the prospect of a BMW-powered Bentley, the Continental coupes or the Azure convertible provide the answer. The Continental R and Azure share the old Turbo R saloon's formidable twin-turbo 385bhp 6.75-litre engine and consequently the decidedly un-regal performance. While there is no way that cars of this size could ever feel truly sporting, agility is not a top priority and there is plenty of sheer grip.

Body styles Coupe **Engine capacity** 6.75V8 Twin Turbo **Price from** £230,000 **Manufactured in** England

Continental RT

Those who crave for yet more performance, together with yet more exclusivity, can take the Continental T. Inside there is a rather tasteless aluminium dashboard, but its 400-plus bhp gives almost Ferrari-like performance.

Body styles Coupe
Engine capacity 4.4V8 Twin Turbo
Price from £230,000
Manufactured in England

Buick Regal

new!

The new Regal is Buick's first real attempt at kicking its retirement-crowd image. Subtle, laid-back styling masks a new, super-stiff, front-drive platform and a line-up of engines that includes a high-adrenaline, supercharged 3.8 V6. Spacious, room-for-five interior is big on luxury, with oodles of leather and walnut. Build quality throughout is impressive.

The supercharged Regal GS is the star here. Packing 240bhp, this wolf in Lamb Chop clothing streaks from standstill to 60mph in just 6.5 seconds. There's handling to match too, with laser-sharp steering and leech-like grip. With a competitive price tag and an impressive tally of standard equipment, the GS is hard to resist.

Best All-Rounder: Regal GS

Body styles	Price from
Saloon	$21,000

Engine capacity	Manufactured in
3.8V6, 3.8V6 Supercharged	United States

Bristol Blenheim

Few people have ever heard of Bristol, but one of Britain's handful of independent car makers still quietly makes its exclusive Blenheim coupes for a small but exclusive circle of buyers. It may use twenty year old technology, but the subtle looks and handmade luxury make it the first choice of a handful of wealthy celebrities.

A recent 'facelift' saw the Blenheim dragged into this decade, with a few essential modern gadgets and a mild cosmetic tweak but the square looks, separate chassis, big Chrysler V8 and typically British interior are still stuck in the seventies. A cheaper Mercedes would walk all over it in most departments, but is nowhere near as exclusive.

Best All-Rounder: Blenheim

Body styles	Price from
Saloon	£118,000

Engine capacity	Manufactured in
5.9V8	England

BMW

It is, without doubt, the company with the image that most manufacturers would like to emulate. BMW has built its success story on an range of cars that combine German quality with a sporting appeal. BMW cars are just better to drive than most of the competition, even with the smallest 1.6-litre engines. Part of that can be put down its insistence on sticking with rear-wheel-drive, which gives steering, handling and a gearchange which just cannot be replicated by a front-driver. But also keeping the enthusiasm high is the never ending development of new models. The big news for 1998/9 is, of course, the new 3-Series, but there is a revised Z3 due in the Spring, an M5 version of the 5-Series and a new 3.0-litre diesel engine.

3-Series Touring

3-Series Convertible

3-Series Coupe

BMW 3-Series   *new!*

It may not look it, but the BMW 3-Series is new from the ground up. A touch more length means improved room inside - a weak point of the outgoing model. There's a predictable range of engines, from a 1.6 four-cylinder through to a 2.8-litre six, but there are some new models too, a smooth 1.8 and, soon, a powerful 2.0-litre direct-injection turbo-diesel.

With just the saloon version currently available there is still enough to keep demand running at an all-time high. It does everything a little better than before, with increased refinement, improved practicality and, of course, lots of driver enjoyment. Still running in the previous style are the Touring, Coupe, Convertible and Compact.

Best All-Rounder: 323i

Body styles Saloon
Engine capacity 1.6, 1.8, 2.5, 2.8, 2.0TDi
Price from £19,800
Manufactured in Germany

3-Series Compact

BMW 5-Series

The handsome looks of the 5-Series are more than skin deep - this remains the pace-setting executive car despite Audi's A6 and Mercedes' E-class. Saloon or estate, and from the humble but impeccably refined 2.0 to the 4.4-litre V8, each 5-Series provides a fine balance of refinement with driving pleasure.

As well as the character of its engines, the 5-Series excels in its ride and handling. The only thing even approaching a weak point is that there is still not as much rear legroom as in its direct rivals, even though this aspect has been improved over the previous generation model. The Touring offers a uniquely sporting driving experience for a big estate, but less load space than direct rivals.

Best All-Rounder: 523i

Body styles
Saloon, Estate

Engine capacity
2.0, 2.5, 2.8, 3.5V8, 4.4V8, 2.5TD

Price from
£24,300

Manufactured in
Germany

BMW 7-Series

As a 'director level' car the 7-Series is long-established as one of the favourites, something that the latest generation continues. Although the entry-level 728i is less than half the price of the top level 750iL, there is very little to visually differentiate one model from another within the 7-Series range, reflecting just how strong the image is. Both the 740i and 750i are available in long wheelbase form.

Compared with its direct rivals the Jaguar XJ8 and Audi A8, the 7-Series lies somewhere in between in its driving experience - not as stiffly sprung as the Audi but firmer than the Jaguar. All the engines are superbly refined and responsive.

Best All-Rounder: 735i

Body styles
Saloon

Engine capacity
2.8, 3.5V8, 4.4V8, 5.4V12, 2.5TD

Price from
£36,900

Manufactured in
Germany

BMW 8-Series

The 8-Series is very much a product of the 1980s, evident in its brash, aggressive styling, particularly when lined up alongside the XK8. Like its competitors, this glamour machine is as big as an executive saloon but its sporting style compromises space utilisation so much that rear seat accommodation is appropriate only for short journeys.

The 4.4-litre V8 gives the car more of a sporting character than the discontinued V12, its lighter weight resulting in better agility. Inside, of course, there is all the luxury you might expect - despite its age this is still an awe-inspiring machine.

Best All-Rounder: 840Ci

Body styles
Coupe

Engine capacity
4.4V8

Price from
£57,500

Manufactured in
Germany

BMW Z3

The Z3 offers everything from the lukewarm to the blistering in terms of performance, but every version has the looks which knock bystanders for six. Now the convertible is joined by a Coupe, offering more in the way of luggage space but remaining strictly a two-seater.

Well built and entertaining, the Z3 really comes into its own with the 2.8-litre six-cylinder version, which offers a broad spread of accessible power. The more realistically-priced 1.9 will be enough fun for most people, offering comfort and a touch of class unequalled by the budget competition. The crazy M Roadster is a licence-loser.

Best All-Rounder: Z3 1.9

Body styles
Convertible, Coupe

Engine capacity
1.8, 1.9, 2.8, 3.2

Price from
£21,500

Manufactured in
United States

cadillac

Cadillac

General Motors' luxury car division is on the up and up. So long the maker of chrome-laden, marshmallow-sprung leviathans, Cadillac is now changing tack. It enters the booming US sport-utility market this year with its XXL-size Escalade 4x4; it unveils a dramatic Chevy Corvette-based sports car concept early next year; and its management is promising a brand new Cadillac every year for the next decade. All of which might help to lower the average age of its target buyer. With its latest Seville, the company is also embarking on an ambitious global sales programme in a bid to supplement its dormant US market.

Cadillac DeVille

Cadillac's best-seller looks like an elegantly restrained four-door cruise ship from the outside. Yet twist the key and this six-seat land yacht is instantly transformed into a jet boat. The range-topping DeVille Concours comes with whisper-quiet 300bhp, 4.6-litre Northstar V8 driving its front wheels. Even the base model offers 275bhp.

With 300bhp and marshmallow suspension, the Concours is definitely a straight-line sprinter but traditional Caddy buyers prefer a ride that's soft and cushiony. With armchair-like seating, acres of stitched leather, and near-silent running, the DeVille is the pinnacle of luxury. The car's OnStar emergency and navigation system will also get you home if you're lost.

Best All-Rounder: DeVille Concours

Body styles Saloon
Engine capacity 4.6V8
Price from $38,000
Manufactured in United States

Cadillac Catera

This, according to Cadillac, is 'The Caddy That Zigs'. The aim: to 'zig' into the hearts of younger, so-called 'baby boomer' buyers. Built in Germany and based on the Opel Omega, the Catera uses the Opel's 24-valve 3.0-litre V6. Styling changes are minor; chrome Cadillac grille, chrome wheels and full-width tail-lights.

As the only Caddy with rear-drive, the Catera is the closest in feel to a Euro sports saloon. Responsive handling, coupled with a firmish, yet smooth ride appeals to non-Cadillac buyers. But 200bhp V6 has to work hard to move this hefty four-door, though the standard four-speed auto masks dull performance with enthusiastic and smooth changes.

Best All-Rounder: Catera V6

Body styles	**Price from**
Saloon	$30,000
Engine capacity	**Manufactured in**
3.0V6	Germany

Cadillac Seville

Bargain-priced American cars sell well in the UK, so General Motors has graced the UK market with its legendary prestige brand. As with all US cars, it is big in every sense of the word with a huge 4.6-litre V8 engine, but it has been tuned well to suit UK roads.

It will take a brave buyer to choose the Caddy over a more established and fashionable European marque, but the Seville will suit some people down to the ground. It has the package you would expect from a US-built car and the power it needs to carry around a mountain of standard equipment.

Best All-Rounder: Cadillac Seville

Body styles
Saloon

Engine capacity
4.6V8

Price from
£40,000

Manufactured in
United States

Cadillac Escalade *new!*

America's MPV market is currently sizzling; that's why Cadillac is jumping in with its first-ever 4x4. Based closely on the strong-selling Chevrolet Tahoe, the Escalade uses the same girder-like chassis and stump-pulling 5.7-litre V8. But the interior is pure Caddy, with glove-soft leather, shiny wood and a killer stereo.

Anyone who owned a 1950s be-finned Cadillac should feel right at home in the Escalade. Vague, finger-light steering, mushy brakes and oil tanker-like bulk do little to enhance the Cadillac image. But there's lots of power, room for five and their luggage, and the ability to get to the 18th green by way of the sand traps.

Best All-Rounder: Cadillac Escalade

Body styles
Estate

Engine capacity
5.7V8

Price from
$44,000

Manufactured in
United States

caterham

Caterham

From its beginnings as a Lotus dealer, Caterham blossomed first from the only outlet sanctioned to sell the Lotus Seven to taking over the manufacture of the car completely after Lotus decided that it did not fit in with its future plans. The company has gone from strength to strength with the Seven, remaining honest to the concept of a simple light-weight sports car that is at home on the track as on the road, yet offering continual worthwhile development. As always it can be built up from a kit of parts, but today's Seven - and its more civilised development, the 21 - can be bought ready for the road too.

Caterham 21

Caterham 21

The 21, Caterham's answer to the Lotus Elise, falls substantially short of the mark. The idea was to take the excellent chassis and engines used in the Seven and clothe them in a more modern and practical body. The quality is not up to it though, and the price is pushed too high to compete.

As with the Seven, the 21 uses Rover's K-Series engines to deliver stunning performance, especially with the SS model's six -speed gearbox and 148bhp powerplant. It has a big boot but otherwise retains all the Seven's uncomfortable quirks and faults while removing some of its thrills.

Body styles Convertible **Engine capacity** 1.6, 1.8
Price from £22,500 **Manufactured in** England

Super Seven

When Lotus decided to cease production of its classic Seven, Caterham Cars stepped in to keep the legend alive and hasn't looked back since. Enthusiasts are constantly grateful - the Seven is the most fun you can have on four wheels, with real race-car responses and supercar performance for minimal money.

The options available are almost endless, and include building the car yourself. The Seven is now available with Rover's excellent K-series engines, including the 143 bhp VVC unit from the MGF, but even the 1.4-litre is fast. Cramped cabins mean a few will be excluded from ever trying one, though.

Body styles Convertible
Engine capacity 1.6, 1.8
Price from £13,300
Manufactured in England

Super Seven

chrysler

Chrysler

The sign of the company headquarters now reads Daimler-Chrysler, following its strategic merger with the German car maker last summer. It is an alliance that can only strengthen Chrysler's position, providing it with greater access to world markets and the ability to tap into Mercedes' extensive supplier base. What won't change is Chrysler's strong emphasis on great design. A new Intrepid luxury saloon, with a body made from recycled plastic Coke bottles, is due in 2001, as is a redesigned Viper supercar. Now wouldn't that perform well with a 6.0-litre Mercedes V12 under the bonnet?

Jeep Grand Cherokee   *new!*

Yes, the shape may look the same, but Chrysler's 1999 Jeep Grand Cherokee is new from the tyres up. Major changes include two new engines, new rear suspension, steering and brakes, an all-new interior and an improved four-wheel drive system. The eagle-eyed will no doubt spot the longer nose, steeper sloping grille and bigger headlights.

This latest Grand Cherokee comes with an all-new 230bhp 4.7-litre V8, replacing the old gas-guzzlin' 5.2. For diesel-lovers, there's also a fresh 3.1-litre five-cylinder turbo, while the trusty 4.0-litre petrol is now quieter and comes with 10 more horsepower. New five-speed auto is a smoother changer, while the improved rear suspension gives a less-turbulent ride.
Best All-Rounder: Grand Cherokee 4.0

Body styles Estate
Engine capacity
4.0, 4.7V8, 3.1TD
Price from
$26,000

**Manufactured
in** United States,
Austria

Chrysler 300M

Chrysler is banking on the 300M's dramatic, cab-forward styling and athletic performance to win friends in Europe's cut-throat luxury car market. That and a new 3.5-litre V6 with Porsche Tiptronic-like AutoStick transmission. Styling is guaranteed to spin heads, while a sexy, leather-clad cabin will please those inside.

A new 3.5 packs a healthy 253bhp punch, allowing the 300M to hold its head high in the performance saloon pack. Responsive steering helps provide entertaining handling and there's a firm, yet comfy ride. Cab-forward design means barn-like interior space and cavernous boot. Bags of personality for the cash.

Best All-Rounder: 300M 3.5

Body styles
Saloon

Engine capacity
3.5V6

Price from
$27,500

Manufactured in
United States

Jeep Cherokee

The car which relaunched the famous Jeep brand back in the UK still has a lot going for it, looking fine value compared to the equivalent Land Rover or Mitsubishi, especially when equipment levels are taken into consideration. Its main drawbacks are its interior space and dated looks.

The 2.5-litre Sport Cherokee looks great value, with air bags, electric windows and ABS as standard, but the engine means makes it sluggish. Conversely the 4.0-litre straight six in the Limited model makes it one of the fastest off-roaders around. The 2.5 turbo-diesel makes an economical tow car and holds its value well.

Best All-Rounder: Cherokee 4.0 Limited

Body styles
Estate

Engine capacity
2.5, 4.0, 2.5TD

Price from
£18,200

Manufactured in
United States

Chrysler LHS

Sister to the sporty 300M, but worlds apart in character. It's a bigger car, offering limo-like comfort in its leather and wood-lined cabin. Striking to look at, with its massive front grille and giant headlamps, the LHS comes with Chrysler's new all-aluminium 3.5-litre, 253bhp V6 driving the front wheels.

Luxury is the name of the game here. Sumptuous interior with stretch-out legroom, and power everything. While the V6 provides athletic performance coupled with whisper-quiet refinement, Americans prefer their land yachts with V8 power. Nevertheless, the LHS is a delight to drive, having secure, responsive handling and a cushy, bump-smoothing ride.

Best All-Rounder: LHS 3.5

Body styles
Saloon

Engine capacity
3.5V6

Price from
$28,200

Manufactured in
United States

Chrysler Sebring Convertible

Here's a full four-seat convertible, with a tight-fitting, fully-lined power roof, great looks, with a breezy, fun-to-drive manner for the equivalent of £13,000. New this year is a super-luxury Limited version, with full leather interior, polished alloys and a Mitsubishi-built 2.5-litre V6 power with four-speed auto.

Release a catch, press a button and watch as the sunlight pours in. Simple as that. And the heavy lining, glass rear window and double sealing means that this is an all-year-round convertible. Despite its length, the Sebring is shudder-free; it rides smoothly and remains composed even on the roughest surfaces.

Best All-Rounder: Sebring JXi

Body styles
Convertible

Engine capacity
2.5V6

Price from
$20,600

Manufactured in
United States

Chrysler Voyager

Americans love their MPVs, but they demand big engines and huge equipment levels all for a cheap price. The seven seat Voyager is willing to oblige, and it now offers UK buyers the same top value package. Long warranties and great residual values are its other main attractions.

The standard Voyager is big enough for most, but if you need more space there is a Grand version which will swallow seven people and their luggage - rare in an MPV. All models have essential air conditioning, but avoid the 2.0-litre version - its wheezy engine just can't cope. The 3.3 V6 is far more pleasant, but thirsty.

Best All-Rounder: Grand Voyager 3.3

Body styles
MPV

Engine capacity
2.4, 3.8, 2.5TD

Price from
£18,400

Manufactured in
United States, Austria

Jeep Wrangler

The archetypal Jeep has come a long way since it was Dwight D. Eisenhower's preferred form of transport. Steadily upgraded over the years, the most recent modifications have given it a smart interior, a standard heater and independent, coil sprung suspension.

It's still a Jeep though, which means a torquey 2.5-litre or a 4.0-litre straight-six which sounds like a NASCAR racer. It burns fuel like one too. The off-road ability hasn't been compromised either, and the Jeep can still cut it with the best in the rough, where, in truth, the suspension is at its most impressive.

Best All-Rounder: Wrangler 4.0 Sport

Body styles
Convertible, Estate

Engine capacity
2.5, 4.0

Price from
£14,200

Manufactured in
United States

Chrysler Neon

Americans expect a lot of car for their cash; the fact that the Neon is small means they don't want to pay a great deal at all. Which is good news when it comes to export - the Neon sports a budget price tag everywhere it's sold.

Naturally, some corners have been cut here and there - both 1.8 and 2.0-litre engines are harsh, if torquey, and some of the trim feels a bit low rent. But, the ride and handling are fine and all versions get power steering and electric windows. As an enjoyable-workhorse on a budget, you could do a lot worse than the Neon.

Best All-Rounder: Neon 2.0 LS

Body styles
Saloon, Coupe

Engine capacity
1.8, 2.0

Price from
£12,000

Manufactured in
United States

Chrysler Viper

If you think the Viper looks outrageous, just wait until you lift the bonnet. Underneath lies the biggest engine currently fitted to any production car, an 8.0-litre V10. As you might expect the power is awesome, but its real beauty is the pulling power in any gear.

Left-hand-drive means its not the most practical of supercars, and its handling can be lethal in the wet, but few cars offer the pose potential or the straight-line speed of the Viper at such a reasonable price. The coupe is more practical but the Targa-topped RT10 roadster is the only choice for real summer thrills.

Best All-Rounder: Viper RT10

Body styles
Coupe, convertible

Engine capacity
8.0V10

Price from
£68,800

Manufactured in
United States

chevrolet

Chevrolet

They call it the 'Heartbeat of America'. With a line-up of cars and trucks that runs from a cheap 'n cheerful Fiesta-sized runabout, though a monster 4x4 Silverado 'dualie' pick-up truck, to a 175mph Corvette, Chevrolet is General Motors' high-volume division. Founded in 1911 by racing driver Louis Chevrolet, the company commands unswerving loyalty among its buyers, particularly in the booming US pick-up market. Mediocre design and a lack of real innovation is, however, beginning to test that loyalty. Example: Chevy's crucial Silverado pick-up was launched last summer with only one rear-hinged side door. Rival Ford and Chrysler pick-ups already had two. Big mistake.

Chevrolet Corvette

First there was the Coupe. Then the Convertible. For '99, America's favourite muscle car debuts in its latest Hardtop form. Lighter than the Coupe, and lacking the lift-out T-top panels, the Hardtop is also reckoned to be the quickest - and least-expensive - of the new fifth-generation Vettes.

Eight cylinders and 345bhp tends to guarantee supercar performance, and the Corvette doesn't disappoint. Zero-to-60mph comes in under five seconds, while flat-out it's good for 175mph. And with a chassis stiffer than Tower Bridge, this is by far the best-handling Vette yet. Comfortable cockpit too. Bose stereo is disco quality.

Best All-Rounder: Corvette Hardtop

Body styles Coupe, Convertible
Engine capacity 5.7V8
Price from £36,700
Manufactured in United States

Chevrolet Blazer

Another top-value package from over the Atlantic, where sports off-roaders are even more popular than in this country. For the price of an entry-level Mitsubishi Shogun, Chevrolet will provide an even bigger five-door 4x4 powered by a 4.3-litre, 200bhp V6 which is loaded with equipment.

The prettier - and cheaper - three-door Blazer is not yet available in the UK, but the five-door is spacious and of course performs well thanks to the torquey and engine and automatic gearbox. On road manners are hampered by the crude suspension though, and by the left-hand-drive only format.

Best All-Rounder: Blazer

Body styles
Estate

Engine capacity
4.3V6

Price from
£22,200

Manufactured in
United States

Chevrolet Camaro

How much is a stylish looking coupe with a 285bhp V8 engine worth? According to Chevrolet it is little more than the price of a large family saloon. The suspension is outdated and the interior trim tacky, but it delivers unbeatable performance per pound.

The awesome six-speed Z28 is the cheapest way of getting to 170mph, but don't expect sophistication. The 200bhp 3.8-litre V6 auto is not as fast but better balanced and even cheaper, and the well-equipped convertible is good value too. The main drawback for British buyers will be the left-hand drive.

Best All-Rounder: Camaro 3.8 Convertible

Body styles
Coupe, Convertible

Engine capacity
3.8V6, 5.7V8

Price from
£18,000

Manufactured in
United States

Chevrolet Malibu

Chevy's prize-fighter, the Mondeo-sized Malibu, aims straight at the heartland of the US car buying market. The styling breaks no new ground, but here buyers care more about price and packaging than smart looks. And the package is undoubtedly great value, with air conditioning, dual airbags and ABS all standard.

With a rock-solid platform, the Malibu is better-built than most low-cost Chevys. The twin cam 2.4-litre four-cylinder is rather harsh and noisy, but provides gutsy performance. Less frenetic is the optional 3.1-litre 155bhp V6. A sweet-changing four-speed auto comes as standard as does nicely-weighted power steering. For the money, it's tough to beat.
Best All-Rounder: Malibu V6

Body styles
Saloon

Engine capacity
2.4, 3.1V6

Price from
$15,700

Manufactured in
United States

Chevrolet Suburban

Stretching almost 19 feet in length and standing close to six feet high, Chevy's Suburban is a monster truck for the road. It's so big that it won't fit into most US garages. Yet Chevy can't build enough of this XXL-sized leviathan for America's style-conscious baby-boomers and Aspen ski-bunnies.

Pick your power; standard 5.7-litre V8, optional 7.4-litre V8, or 6.5-litre turbo-diesel. Each offers enough muscle to uproot tree stumps or tow the QE2. There's seating for nine on three bench seats, though luggage space is limited because the rear seat doesn't fold flat. For mums who hate the minivan image, a Suburban is the kiddy-carrier of choice.
Best All-Rounder: Suburban 5.7

Body styles
Estate

Engine capacity
5.7V8, 7.4V8, 6.5TD

Price from
$25,600

Manufactured in
United States

citroen

citröen

Citroen

Aficionados used to love the quirky character of Citroens, but that has largely disappeared in today's cars, which bear a strong family relationship to Peugeots of the same size. The result is that not enough of the range really has any compelling qualities above its competitors - Citroens are good but not great cars. 1999 sees an important new common-rail direct-injection turbo diesel for the Xantia, a mild face-lift for the Synergie, and a mini MPV based upon the Xsara. The replacement for the XM is still at least a couple of years away.

Citroen Xsara

The old ZX was never completely outclassed in the small-medium sector, but it lacked the flair and innovation with which Citroen used to be associated. Sadly, the Xsara continues this trend. All three body styles are unremarkable in their appearance and the interiors, although functional, are fairly nondescript.

It's the same story with the engines, which drive well enough but are notable neither for their refinement or performance - 2.0-16v apart. For the moment then, the chassis is the best part of the Xsara. A pillowy smooth ride, crisp steering and fluid handling show that Citroen hasn't lost its talents; merely its verve.

Best All-Rounder: Xsara 1.6 LX 5dr

Body styles Hatchback, Coupe, Estate
Engine capacity 1.4, 1.6, 1.8. 2.0, 1.9D, 1.9TD
Price from £11,700
Manufactured in France

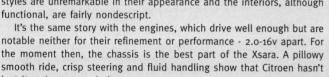

R348 NWP

Citroen Xantia

A recent facelift has kept the essential fleet market interested in the stylish but ageing Citroen, but it can't disguise a car that is now behind the class leaders. However the interiors are spacious and comfortable, especially the estates, and Hydractive suspension ensures a good ride with standard self-levelling for those who tow or carry heavy loads.

The turbo-diesel Xantias have always been the most popular and it is easy to see why. Refined, powerful and economical they overshadow the lack-lustre petrol engines. The recent addition of a powerful V6 and adaptive auto gearbox has made the good value top-of-the range Exclusive model worth a look. Estates are spacious and practical.

Best All-Rounder: Xantia 2.1TD Estate

Body styles	Price from
Hatchback, Estate	£13,300

Engine capacity	Manufactured in
1.6, 1.8, 2.0, 2.0Turbo, 3.0V6, 1.9TD, 2.1TD	France

Citroen XM

Citroen's largest car is also the most quirky, with wedge styling, air suspension and a hatchback. This is reflected in its popularity, as only a few hundred are sold each year and values plummet on the used market. It is not without qualities though, with a smooth ride and mile-munching motorway ability.

Although the V6 Exclusive versions are fast and well equipped, it is the 2.1 and 2.5-litre turbo-diesels which are the stars of the range, with economy and reasonable performance. The interiors are fragile and take some getting used to, but estate versions are capable of carrying more load than some vans.

Best All-Rounder: XM 2.5 VSX Estate.

Body styles	Price from
Hatchback, Estate	£22,200

Engine capacity	Manufactured in
2.0, 2.0 Turbo, 3.0V6, 2.1TD, 2.5TD	France

Citroen Synergie/Evasion

VW and Ford have proven that two companies can agree an attractive design for an MPV, but Citroen, Peugeot, Fiat and Lancia seemed to have missed the boat. The van-like looks of the Synergie and its cousins hide a competent seven-seater which offers comfort and an easy drive once you get used to the odd gearchange.

Engine choice is petrol or turbo-diesel, both of which suit the Synergie well. Sliding rear side doors can be useful in a tight parking space, but access to the rear-most seats is never easy. Luggage space is worse than most with the rear seats in use.

Best All-Rounder: Synergie 1.9TD

Body styles	Price from
MPV	£16,600

Engine capacity	Manufactured in
1.8, 2.0, 2.0Turbo, 1.9TD, 2.1TD	France

Citroen Saxo

In the world of the enjoyable supermini, the French delight in market domination. Citroen's effort, the Saxo, is little more than a re-hashed Peugeot 106, though that needn't be a bad thing - its range of small engines drives one of the best chassis in the class.

Both hatchback body styles, with or without power steering, are enjoyable and comfortable to drive, despite a cramped driver's footwell. Space in the back isn't great for the class either, and the build quality doesn't have the perceived integrity of some rivals. But on the occasions that the roads get twisty or bumpy, that's easy to overlook.

Best All-Rounder: Saxo 1.4 SX

Body styles
Hatchback

Engine capacity
1.0, 1.1, 1.4, 1.6, 1.5D

Price from
£8,400

Manufactured in
France

Citroen Berlingo Multispace   *new!*

Based on the popular Berlingo van, the Multispace is supposed to appeal to the young as a practical lifestyle vehicle. Its happy nature is complemented by a smooth 1.8-litre petrol engine, bright metallic paint, power steering and the world's largest electric sunroof.

Performance is acceptable and the compliant ride can be enjoyed from five large seats which have excellent visibility. The cabin has plentiful oddments space and the big boot contains a washable rubber mat for convenience. If only it had five-doors and air-conditioning, the Multispace could really compete as a cheap alternative to some MPVs and estate cars.

Best All-Rounder: Multispace 1.8

Body styles
Estate

Engine capacity
1.6, 1.8, 1.9D

Price from
£12,000

Manufactured in
France

daihatsu

Daihatsu

Daihatsu is master of the niche market, exporting a wider range of small cars from Japan than any other manufacturer. The question is, can it make that big jump into big-volume sales, as it surely needs to do to survive in the longer term?

It certainly won't if it continues with oddball ideas like the Cuore, Move and Terios, that's for sure, but it just might with its latest new entrant into the supermini market, the Sirion. This car has a lot to offer and deserves to be taken seriously. It seems a pity, then, that Daihatsu has largely ignored the Fourtrak off-roader, at one time the mainstay of the range, while phasing out the once popular Sportrak.

Daihatsu Sirion   *new!*

Daihatsu's latest supermini is it's most promising yet. Distinctive without being weird, the Sirion offers an impressive combination of virtues and its three-cylinder engine is remarkably economical. There is a fair degree of refinement for such a small car - the ride and noise levels are both good. Interior space and comfort are reasonable too and, in the UK at least, equipment levels are impressive, with power steering and twin airbags.

The downsides are relatively minor. Performance is hardly lively, and the interior is drab, despite obvious attempts to liven it up. These weaknesses weigh lightly against a car which is priced so competitively.

Best All-Rounder: Sirion

Body styles
Hatchback
Engine capacity
1.0
Price from
£8,000
Manufactured in
Japan

Daihatsu Cuore

One of Daihatsu's many city cars, the Cuore has a bizarre model line-up. Three 659cc engines are offered, two with three-cylinders, of which one is turbocharged. The other unit is a turbocharged four with the same 64bhp as the turbocharged three. Daihatsu offers various three and five-door body styles as well as 4WD for the turbos. Confused?

In fact the best bet has the fourth engine, a basic 850cc 54bhp which is the range's mainstay, offering no-frills urban transport at a low price. The engine is frugal and willing, the interior is basic and cheap but acceptable. Driving is a cinch around town, a chore in the country.

Best All-Rounder: Cuore

Body styles	Price from
Hatchback	£6,500

Engine capacity	Manufactured in
850, 650, 650 turbo	Japan

Daihatsu Terios

The UK TV advert for the Terios' says it all: 'It's small, yet TALL'. It's supposed to be the replacement for the Sportrak, but the off-road ability of that car has been mostly supplanted by urban chic. No serious off-roader can have a revvy 1.3-litre petrol unit delivering its peak torque at more than 5,000rpm.

The tiny four-wheel-drive machine does at least offer the commanding driving position of a proper off-roader and, to be fair, it can reach places that a family saloon won't. It will get strange looks getting there though and the on-road driving experience is compromised with too much bounce and roll as a result.

Best All-Rounder: Terios +

Body styles
Estate

Engine capacity
1.3

Price from
£12,200

Manufactured in
Japan

Daihatsu Charade

With the rest of the Daihatsu range looking so interesting, it is easy to overlook the anonymous Charade. The range of two five-door hatchbacks and one saloon are easy to drive and reasonably spacious, but it is the warranty package and legendary Daihatsu reliability which will attract most buyers.

All Charades arrive complete with a driver's airbag and power steering, but the better-value GLXi adds air conditioning, central locking and electric windows. The five-door model is only available with the perky 1.3-litre engine, while the range topping saloon gets the torquier 1.5-litre unit.

Best All-Rounder: Charade 1.3GLXi

Body styles
Hatchback, Saloon

Engine capacity
1.0, 1.3, 1.5, 1.6

Price from
£9,000

Manufactured in
Japan

Daihatsu Grand Move

Daihatsu has aimed the Grand Move at the growing demand for recreational vehicles which answer a number of needs from family to fun. There's plenty of space inside, with real comfort for four or five, and a large boot. The Grand Move is easy to use in town too, with power steering and an incredibly tight turning circle.

But the downsides are too strong, especially compared with the Renault Scenic. The rear bench seat lacks the versatility of the removable individual seats of the Scenic. The interior is flooded with beige and brown plastic which looks cheap and tacky. And the 1.5-litre engine isn't man enough for the job.

Best All-Rounder: Grand Move

Body styles	**Price from**
Estate	£11,500
Engine capacity	**Manufactured in**
1.5	Japan

Daihatsu Move

Designed to provide the maximum space for its occupants in the shortest overall length, the Move instead has grown upwards with a result that even Daihatsu will admit looks weird. There's just one engine, a gruff three-cylinder 850cc unit, which offers good economy but little in the way of performance if there is more than the driver on board.

In the front, the height of the Move seems daft, but rear seat passengers sit higher to improve legroom and visibility. The Move is reasonably comfortable, and around town it's quite fun for a short while, but in the country the lack of performance, and the susceptibility to side winds, makes it all too tiring.

Best All-Rounder: Move

Body styles
Hatchback

Engine capacity
850

Price from
£7,200

Manufactured in
Japan

Daihatsu Fourtrak

Daihatsu's 'proper' off-roader has always appealed to buyers looking for a workhorse because of its no-nonsense attitude off the road and lack of refinement on it. Despite newer and more attractive looking competition, the Fourtrak will remain popular with farmers because of its ability in the mud, huge towing capacity, and faultless reliability in all weathers.

The Fourtrak is only available with one engine option - a fine performing a 2.8-litre turbo-diesel. It has great pulling power for sticky situations or towing, and is also a relaxed motorway cruiser. Top models are well equipped but pricey, and there is no five-door model. Most buyers plump for the no-frills entry-level car.

Best All-Rounder: Fourtrak TDL

Body styles
Estate

Engine capacity
2.8TD

Price from
£15,000

Manufactured in
Japan

daewoo

Daewoo

Daewoo had a tough entry to the world car market, selling re-bodied versions of Vauxhalls and Opels that were already years out of date. But cleverly the cars were developed sufficiently to prevent them being awful, and, helped by a fantastic after-sales package, sold well in the UK. Now with an entirely new range of cars available, they're still not the best, but it's a step in the right direction. Importantly customers are still looked after well, which they seem to love.

Daewoo Matiz   *new!*

City cars tend to have many oddities, but as an increasing number of makers enter the fray, so the peculiarities lessen. The Matiz is Daewoo's first attempt and a fine effort it is too. From the perky styling to the mini-MPV interior, it shows the way to others who have been in this market for years.

Powered by an 800cc three-cylinder engine, there's a throbby hum but not much in the way of performance. That aside, the interior will genuinely take four six-footers comfortably, the dashboard is as good as the best superminis and the Matiz is quite fun to drive. At the price it's outstanding value.

Best All-Rounder: Matiz SE

Body styles
Hatchback
Engine capacity
800
Price from
£6,300
Manufactured in
Korea

Daewoo Nubira

The Nubira is available in saloon, estate and five-door hatch forms, although not every version is sold in every country. A medium-sized family car, it majors on offering plenty of value and space for the money. To keep down costs, the engine range is restricted to just 1.6 and 2.0-litre petrol units.

This is the first Daewoo designed in the UK and it shows. The Nubira has a European feel that is absent from its sister models - it has well weighted steering, positive controls, a compliant ride and tidy handling. Coupled to good accommodation and the sales package, the Nubira is a viable proposition.

Best All-Rounder: Nubira 2.0 CDX

Body styles	Price from
Saloon, Estate	£12,000
Engine capacity	**Manufactured in**
1.6, 2.0	Korea

Daewoo Lanos

The Lanos is priced almost as keenly as the Nexia it replaces and offers a wider range of engines and trim levels to broaden its appeal. Available as a three or five-door hatchback and a neat saloon, the impressive specification includes two new engines, a 1.4-litre and 1.6-litre.

The Lanos feels reasonably well put together, despite the cheap plastics inside. But it is neither refined enough for this class, nor is it good to drive, with a 1.4 engine that doesn't sparkle, and a coarse 1.6. As before, the key factor in buying this Daewoo is the deal, but there are better budget buys around.

Best All-Rounder: Lanos 1.4 SE

Body styles
Hatchback, Saloon
Engine capacity
1.4, 1.6
Price from
£8,800
Manufactured in
Korea

Daewoo Leganza

It's harder to go upmarket than down, but Daewoo has graduated into the full-sized family car sector with its Leganza, a category ruled by trusted brands like Ford and GM. The Daewoo comes, as ever, armed with bags of equipment and the best after-sales package in the business.

For the keen driver the Leganza falls a bit flat, with an engine too course when revved and soft handling. But others will appreciate the amount of space front and back, the comfort and the lack of noise when cruising. It is well finished as well, making it a Daewoo you don't have to justify to your friends.

Best All-Rounder: Leganza 2.0 SX

Body styles
Saloon
Engine capacity
2.0
Price from
£13,800
Manufactured in
Korea

Ferrari

There was a time when making a decision between a Ferrari and a Porsche was simple. You bought a Ferrari with your heart, a Porsche with your head. Now the situation is far less clear cut, for a Ferrari is a far more practical proposition than ever before. Sure, there is still excitement and brio unmatched by any other supercar maker, but it is now laced with an attention to detail in the design and manufacture with the result that the late 1990s Ferrari can be used for business as well as pleasure. Not that many do, however. Most owners still tuck them away in centrally heated garages to be brought out a dozen times each year. Shame.

Targa

Ferrari F355

This is what many people associate with Ferrari. A sleek, low, mid-engined two-seater, preferably in red. It is the cheapest Ferrari too, though today that still means 50 percent more than a Porsche 911. Just one engine option is available, but three body styles are on offer - coupe (Berlinetta), targa (GTS) or convertible (Spider).

The F355's 3.5-litre V8 produces 380bhp, making it one of the highest bhp-per-litres of any normally-aspirated road car. The engine has a range of gloriously purposeful sounds, and there is a real joy to be found just whipping up and down the rev range, clicking the gearlever through its aluminium housing. With finely-tuned handling, driving the F355 is a remarkably tactile experience.

Best All-Rounder: F355 Berlinetta

Body styles Coupe, Targa, Convertible
Engine capacity 3.5V8
Price from £99,000
Manufactured in Italy

Spider

F355

Ferrari 456M

Pininfarina is Ferrari's favourite designer, and with the 456M it is easy to see why. The first front-engined Ferrari for years, it combines elegance with the subtlest of hints at the astounding performance that is contained within. Although designated Ferrari's Grand Tourer rather than an out and out sports car, that doesn't mean any lack of performance. The 442bhp V12 engine can propel this two-plus-two seater up to 186mph.

The 456M belies its race car-breeding when driven hard, too. A rear-mounted transaxle helps keep the weight evenly distributed and makes for an agility way out of keeping for its size. As a four-seater it is really a bit of joke, but otherwise this is the most practical Ferrari on offer.

Best All-Rounder: 456GT

Body styles	Price from
Coupe	£168,000

Engine capacity	Manufactured in
5.5V12	Italy

Ferrari 550M

At the time it seemed strange that Ferrari should revert to a front engine for its Testarossa/512M replacement. Yet it makes some sense, for the 550M is a more practical machine that technological advances have ensured offers everything and more in terms of driving prowess than the old mid-engined models ever could.

The huge power output helps. The 485bhp on tap ensures the 550 Maranello brushes the magic 200 mph and hits 60mph in just over 4 seconds. State-of-the art traction control keeps thing in check. Inside there's a new feeling of quality and luxury, though for many it will still be the howl of that V12 that is the most important aspect of any Ferrari.

Best All-Rounder: 550M

Body styles	Price from
Coupe	£150,000

Engine capacity	Manufactured in
5.5V12	Italy

Fiat

Fiat is one of the 'Big Six' European car manufacturers and as the dominant brand in Italy it naturally covers every end of the spectrum. So Fiat buyers can choose anything from a tiny town car to affordable sports car to people carrier. On the world stage Fiat has developed a car - the Palio - that may look like a modern hatchback but is simple enough to be manufactured by far less technologically-advanced nations. The one area where Fiat has failed to make any real impact is the luxury and executive sectors, but then as Alfa Romeo, Lancia and Maserati are also owned by the company, perhaps there is little need. Oh, and of course, Fiat also owns Ferrari....

Marea Saloon

Marea Weekend

Brava

Fiat Bravo/Brava/Marea

Three different names, but the same car in three-door, five-door and saloon/estate forms, with the Bravo intended to be rather sportier in appeal than the five-door Brava. There is a wide range of petrol and diesel engines, including, in the Marea, an impressive five-cylinder 125bhp turbo-diesel.

The interior is distinctive and comfortable, although rear headroom is limited in the hatchbacks. The Marea, particularly in Weekend (estate) form offers the most space, though all variants are refined and pleasing to drive. But it is the style that is major selling point with these cars. Deep down they are rather ordinary.

Best All-Rounder: Brava 1.6 SX

Body styles Hatchback, Saloon, Estate
Engine capacity 1.4, 1.6, 1.8, 2.0, 1.9TD, 2.4TD
Price from £10,900
Manufactured in Italy

Bravo

Fiat Seicento

new!

Gone are the sharp edges of the Cinquecento. Its replacement, the Seicento, softens the approach, with a blend of curves and nice detailing. The interior is a delight of Mickey Mouse switches and buttons, with plenty of stowage space. Room inside for people is tight, but the seats themselves are pretty comfortable, while noise is well suppressed.

But is has some significant weaknesses too. The brakes are too heavy, the pedals - in right-hand-drive cars - cramped and the performance of the 900cc model is pedestrian. The 1.1 Sporting overcomes this last problem, and with its tauter suspension, is the more pleasing car.

Best All-Rounder: Seicento Sporting

Body styles	Price from
Hatchback	£6,500

Engine capacity	Manufactured in
900, 1.1	Poland

Fiat barchetta

Fiat's little barchetta roadster is very popular in mainland Europe, but less so in the UK. That's because, despite undercutting most of its rivals, it comes in left-hand-drive only. It's a shame, because the 1.8-litre barchetta is a cracking car to drive.

The chic styling is combined with a well designed interior which shouts Latin flair. The characterful 1.8-litre engine does the same, driving through the front wheels with enthusiasm and vigour. A pleasant gearbox, composed ride and communicative steering all enhance the appeal of a car with few proper faults, allowing dismissal of features like awkward door-handles simply as characterful touches.

Best All-Rounder: barchetta 1.8

Body styles
Convertible

Engine capacity
1.8

Price from
£15,800

Manufactured in
Italy

Fiat Punto

Fiat's supermini scooped a Car of the Year award on its launch, and it's easy to see why. The distinctive body houses an interior which set new standards for space. New engines have made the Punto even more economical and, as with all Fiats, it is well equipped compared to similarly-priced rivals.

All normally-aspirated Puntos are now fitted with an all-new 16-valve 1.2-litre engine, with power outputs of 60 or 85bhp. Both engines are perky and economical. The 1.4-litre turbocharged GT model is fast but hard work to drive. The turbo-diesels are economical but feel heavy, while the cabrio is an almost unique offering in this size of car.

Best All-Rounder: Punto 60S

Body styles
Hatchback, convertible

Engine capacity
1.1, 1.2, 1.4 Turbo, 1.7TD

Price from
£7,800

Manufactured in
Italy

Fiat Coupe

In a market where style counts, the distinctive Fiat was bound to win friends. Even now it still turns heads, and the interior is equally distinctive. The front-wheel drive chassis will appeal to those promoted from hot-hatches, and the reasonably-sized boot and rear seats mean they won't have to give up all the practicality.

Both Coupe models are now fitted with five-cylinder 20-valve engines. The non-turbo produces 147bhp and is a pleasant and well-balanced car to drive, but the turbo is a real stormer, with 220bhp and shattering mid-range punch for overtaking. The chassis can struggle to cope though, and is a handful in the wet.

Best All-Rounder: Coupe 20-valve

Body styles
Coupe

Engine capacity
2.0, 2.0 Turbo

Price from
£20,200

Manufactured in
Italy

Fiat Multipla   *new!*

Fiat has never been a company to follow fashion, so its Renault Megane rival is extremely odd looking inside and out. Besides the looks, its most interesting feature is the seating pattern - six people are sat on two benches with the option of three passengers up front.

The Multipla will just reach Britain in time for Christmas, using the Bravo hatchback range as its base to ensure it is reasonable to drive. Only a 1.6-litre petrol or 1.9-litre turbo-diesel engine will initially be available. Prices are expected to be competitive with the Scenic, starting from around £13,000.

Best All-Rounder: Too early to tell.

Body styles
MPV

Engine capacity
1.6, 1.9TD

Price from
£13,000

Manufactured in
Italy

Fiat Ulysse

Fiat got together with Citroen and Peugeot to bring about this spacious MPV which appeals with its practical seating arrangements and good value. Sliding rear doors are useful in tight spaces, but mean that rear seat passengers can't open the windows. Dash-mounted gearlever and odd handbrake are reminders that the Ulysse is based closely on a van.

The engine choices are limited to a 2.0-litre petrol or a 1.9-litre turbo-diesel and both are sluggish when the car is laden. As a seven seater it's reasonably spacious, but none of the models are as easy to drive or car-like on the road as rivals from Ford, VW and Seat.

Best All-Rounder: Ulysse 2.0 EL

Body styles
MPV

Engine capacity
2.0, 1.9TD

Price from
£17,200

Manufactured in
France

Fiat Palio

The Palio is Fiat's world car, built, or with plans to be built, in Brazil, Argentina, Poland, Turkey, India, China, Chile, Egypt, Morocco, South Africa and Venezuela. By the year 2000 the production rate should reach a staggering million cars a year.

Similar in size to the Fiat Punto, the Palio comes is six different body styles, three and five-door hatchbacks, saloon, estate, van and pick-up. Mechanically, it is simpler than cars for Western Europe, with fewer parts, a higher ground clearance to cope with worse roads and a design which is pitched towards more labour intensive factories. Only the estate may come to Europe.

Best All-Rounder: Too early to tell

Body styles
Hatchback, Saloon, Estate

Engine capacity
1.0, 1.2, 1.5, 1.6, 1.7TD

Price from
n.a.

Manufactured in
Worldwide

ford

Ford

It still seems a little odd that mainstream manufacturer Ford has developed into a design leader, but that's the way things have worked out. While some makers produce just one radical model, Ford has a whole raft of them, and we should applaud the company for the risk-taking which makes motoring all the more interesting. The Focus is the latest in the line, but the last couple of years have seen launches of the Cougar, Puma and Ka, each a ground-breaker in its own way. One of Ford's secrets is to keep the bits you don't see on these cars as simple as possible, so underneath the Cougar hides a Mondeo, under the Ka and Puma a Fiesta. The Focus is all new, and even Ford is hedging its bets with this one, keeping the Escort in production for a couple of years until the more conservative buyers are convinced.

Ford Focus   *new!*

There's no risk of anyone accusing Ford of being unadventurous. The "New Edge" design of the Focus is highly distinctive, its tall stance and long wheelbase providing an interior nearly as spacious as the Mondeo. Ford hopes it will appeal to a broader range of customers than the Escort.

By early 1999 there will be full range of body styles, plus a new powerful 1.6 and a direct-injection turbo-diesel. Safety features abound but even so, Ford pushes the fun-to-drive character which it has exploited so well in recent models. Once buyers become accustomed to the looks, there is every chance the Focus will become a number one seller.

Best All-Rounder: Too early to tell

Body styles
Hatchback, Saloon, Estate
Engine capacity
1.4, 1.6, 1.8, 2.0, 1.8TD
Price from
£12,000 (est)
Manufactured in
Germany, Spain

Focus

Ford Ka

Bold and distinctive inside and out, the Ka adds some real panache to the city car market. It comes in three variants: Ka, Ka2 and Ka3, each adding a few worthwhile options. The 1.3 engine is the same in all though, one of oldest in Ford's armoury, but reasonably refined nonetheless.

Space in the front is fine, but room for rear passengers and luggage is restricted. The bold, clutter free facia is easy to use and the whole car exudes an air of purpose and fun. It's just as good on the road too, where sharp steering and handling help justify the fairly steep asking price.

Best All-Rounder: Ka

Body styles
Hatchback

Engine capacity
1.3

Price from
£8,000

Manufactured in
Spain

Ford Fiesta

Ford took a big step with the face-lifted Fiesta, making it fun to drive and refined. It's paid off as the little car regularly tops sales charts. The chassis is remarkably capable for a small mass-produced car, and quality is top-notch for the class too. Only a lack of rear space and small boot lets the side down.

Entry-level Fiestas use the aged 1.3-litre engine, but it is the Zetec engines, in both 1.25 and 1.4-litre sizes, which add a real zing and match the chassis perfectly. Ghia models are pricey but have equipment levels usually expected only in bigger cars - the diesel is unrefined and best avoided.

Best All-Rounder: Fiesta 1.25 LX 5dr

Body styles
Hatchback

Engine capacity
1.25, 1.3, 1.4, 1.8D

Price from
£8,000

Manufactured in
England, Spain

Ford Escort

With its replacement, the Focus, now on sale, it may seem a little curious that Ford is still making the Escort. But Ford has had its fingers burned before with cars with a radically new design, so the Escort remains for the time being for conservative customers.

It is the UK's best selling car, a position it hardly deserved on merit in the past, though the later Escorts are solid contenders. They have a good feeling of quality and comfort, as well as room for four adults. These Escorts are good to drive too, with power steering on most models and suspension that is sharp enough to provide an enjoyable yet comfortable drive.

Best All-Rounder: Escort 1.6 LX

Body styles
Hatchback, Saloon, Estate

Engine capacity
1.3, 1.4, 1.6, 1.8, 1.8TD

Price from
£10,300

Manufactured in
England, Germany, India

Ford Mondeo

Ford's family car is now two years on from its last makeover and is still Britain's favourite. The fleet market has a lot to do with this, but there are strong reasons for any buyer to choose one. Sit in the driver's seat and everything falls to hand. There's plenty of head and legroom in the front, while space is now better in the back thanks to a redesign of both front and rear seats.

On the road everything feels just as good. The controls are reassuringly positive, there is good visibility, a slick gearchange and a crisp throttle response. Only the four-cylinder engines are the real weak points.

Best All-Rounder: Mondeo 1.8 GLX

Body styles
Hatchback, Saloon, Estate

Engine capacity
1.6, 1.8, 2.0, 2.5V6, 1.8TD

Price from
£14,700

Manufactured in
Belgium

Ford Puma

From a company on a roll in terms of design comes the distinctive Puma coupe. Initially available only with a 1.7-litre 16-valve engine, now the 1.4-litre unit from the Fiesta (which also lends its chassis to the Puma) has been installed too. The two variants are indistinguishable unless you look under the bonnet.

The driving experience of the two display close similarities too. The willing engines are mated to a really sharp chassis and steering and handling are by far the best in the class. Accommodation is a little cramped, but when the Puma drives like it does and costs so little, it really doesn't really matter that much.

Best All-Rounder: Puma 1.7

Body styles
Coupe

Engine capacity
1.4, 1.7

Price from
£13,400

Manufactured in
Germany

Ford Cougar   *new!*

Ford's altogether more promising replacement for the Probe coupe is the Cougar. Like the Probe it is built in the States, but this car is based around the Mondeo running gear, suitably modified to give a more sporting drive. Engines are familiar - 2.0-litre or 2.5 V6.

In either form the Cougar is good to drive, with smooth engine response coupled to fabulous steering and handling. It is a big car overall, lacking the compact feel of a Fiat Coupe, but that helps rear space which, though tight, is passable for adults for a short while. There is also a massive boot beneath the hatchback bodystyle.

Best All-Rounder: Cougar V6

Body styles
Cougar

Engine capacity
2.0, 2.5V6

Price from
£18,000 (est)

Manufactured in
United States

Ford Galaxy

Unsurprisingly Ford's MPV offering has consistently outsold its cousin models from Volkswagen and Seat in the UK, despite the fact that it's hardly any cheaper and it loses value quicker than the Sharan or Alhambra. Just about the only other differences between the Ford and the others are the petrol engines, badges and steering wheels.

Since its launch in '95, the Galaxy has been heralded as one of the nicest MPVs to drive and that's still true. The airline-like cabin seats are upright but comfortable, space is commodious and performance is fine. The Galaxy is a great way to move seven people with (a little) luggage, but its rivals deserve a look too.

Best All-Rounder: Galaxy TDi 110

Body styles
MPV

Engine capacity
2.0, 2.3, 2.8V6, 1.9TDi

Price from
£17,700

Manufactured in
Portugal

Ford Explorer

Offering real US muscle with its 4.0-litre, 206 bhp V6, it's not just the engine that is big - everything about the Explorer is huge, both inside and out. There's enough room for the largest occupants, but petite drivers fit too. Boot space is cavernous.

The leather interior is comfortable, although the flat seats in the rear provide little support. Performance of the V6, coupled to 5-speed automatic transmission, is very strong for a 4x4, and the Explorer is an easy car to drive with great visibility. But despite the leather, the interior lacks class and the clang when the doors shut would disgrace a Fiesta, let alone £25,000-worth of Explorer.

Best All-Rounder: Explorer 4.0

Body styles
Estate

Engine capacity
4.0V6, 4.9V8

Price from
£26,300

Manufactured in
United States

ford usa

Ford USA

Ford is on a roll in the US. Profits are soaring, new models are going well and sales have never been stronger. The company's dynamic management team isn't afraid to make changes either, like dropping slow-selling models to allow for increased production on the top sellers. Ford has also followed Chrysler's lead in realising the importance of eye-catching design. Models like the Cougar, the F150 pick-up, the latest Town Car and new Windstar are recent stand-outs. With the recent hiring of the talented VW Beetle-designer J. Mays as worldwide design chief, expect more dramatic designs.

Ford Contour

Tight rear-seat legroom is still hurting sales of Ford's US version of the European Mondeo. Even the arrival of the sizzling 195bhp Contour SVT from Ford's performance division has done little to change the lacklustre image of this fine-handling four-door. Rumour is that the axe will fall in 2000.

Space may be tight in the back, but on the road, the Contour, and its Mercury sister, the Mystique, never fail to impress. Like its Euro cousin, the Contour is powered by the 125bhp 2.0-litre Zetec four-cylinder, with the smooth-spinning 170bhp 2.5 V6 an option. The SVT is a BMW-basher.

Best All-Rounder: Contour LX 2.0

Body styles Saloon
Engine capacity 2.0, 2.5V6
Price from $14,500
Manufactured in United States

Ford Taurus

No longer America's best-selling car, the ovoid-shaped Taurus is due for a major facelift in '99, waving goodbye to some of the unloved oval styling cues. Almost the same length as a Mercedes S-Class, the Taurus offers seating for six people and their luggage. In addition to the saloon, there's an even-more striking estate version.

Taurus buyers get a choice of two 3.0-litre V6s and a muscley 3.4 V8 developed by Yamaha. None are perfect; the base overhead-valve 3.0-litre is too noisy, the 24-valve 3.0-litre lacks low-down strength, while the V8 is too thirsty. But this rounded four-door corners enthusiastically, grips hard and rides smoothly.
Best All-Rounder: Taurus LX

Body styles	**Price from**
Saloon	$18,000
Engine capacity	**Manufactured in**
3.0V6, 3.4V8	United States

Ford Mustang

America's best-selling muscle car gets some more muscle for '99 - and a more-muscley look. Bigger wheelarches, bigger side scoops and new slim, wrap-around headlamps make up the exterior changes. Under the bonnet, the 3.8-litre V6 gets 40 more ponies taking it to 190bhp, while the 4.6 V8 gets an extra 25 horses, pushing it up to 250bhp.

When it comes to American sports cars, power is everything. With those additional 25 horses, the '99 V8 'Stang smokes its rear tyres easier than ever. Want more power - try the 305bhp Cobra. But even the V6 is a blast to drive in a crude, vintage kind of way.
Best All-Rounder: Mustang GT 4.6

Body styles
Coupe, convertible

Engine capacity
3.8V6, 4.6V8

Price from
$16,250

Manufactured in
United States

Ford Windstar

A victim of the minivan 'door wars' - it had one sliding side door, where rivals had two - Ford's Windstar enters '99 fully face-lifted and with the required dual sliding side doors. The new Windstar's side doors are also power-operated, opening at the touch of a button - an industry first.

Body stiffness has been increased 30 per cent, improving on the Windstar's already fine road manners. The base 3.0-litre is a rather gutless wonder - much livelier is the optional 200bhp 3.8 V6. Reversing becomes easier with the new sonar sensors in the rear bumper alerting the driver to objects behind.
Best All-Rounder: Windstar LX 3.8

Body styles
MPV

Engine capacity
3.0V6, 3.8V6

Price from
$18,200

Manufactured in
United States

ford australia

Ford Australia

1999 is a big year for Ford Australia. The launch of its new AU Falcon range late in 1998 will surely swing some interest away from the rival Holden Commodore, between them the biggest-hitters in the domestic market. The Falcon is sold in a number of guises ranging from the base model, badged Forte, through to the more luxurious Fairmont and sporty Tickford-developed XR6 and XR8 saloons. Estate versions are launched concurrently, with luxury Fairlane and LTD models using the same long-wheelbase platform due in March 1999. Ford's other local models include the Korean-sourced Festiva, Mazda-based Laser and imported Mondeo.

Laser

Mondeo

Festiva

Ford Falcon   *new!*

Launched in September 1998 the all-new AU Falcon promises an extensively tested, lighter car that will be both more economical and quicker than the outgoing model. Interior space is better than before and slightly larger than the rival Commodore VT.

The Ford is retains the current 4.0-litre six cylinder engine in a revised form; there is an option of a 5.0 V8 sourced from the US on some versions. Rear-wheel-drive is also retained with most models making do with a rigid rear axle to contain costs and to appeal to fleet buyers - only the luxury and sports models get full independent suspension.

Best All-Rounder: Falcon Futura

Body styles Saloon, Estate
Engine capacity 4.0, 5.0V8
Price from Aus $ 30,000
Manufactured in Australia

Falcon

Holden Commodore

General Motor's Holden is currently celebrating its 50th anniversary with a range of cars covering the main-stream market, a mix of locally built and imported models. Criticism from some quarters that the large Commodore is now too heavy and therefore too slow and thirsty has encouraged Holden to embark upon a weight-loss programme for the Series II model due in January 1999. A lighter, slight faster and more economical car is anticipated. The luxury long-wheelbase Statesman and Caprice versions of the VT should appear in June 1999. Holden's other passenger cars are sourced from the Opel range, and comprise the Barina (Corsa) Astra and Vectra. Local Vectra production began late in 1998.

Astra

Barina

Vectra

Holden Commodore

Holden launched its slightly larger VT Commodore in '97 to compete more squarely with Ford's Falcon. Loosely based upon the Opel Omega, the rear-drive Commodore is the best selling car in Australia with the majority of its sales coming from the fleet market.

Independent rear suspension is now standard across the sedan and estate range, with power coming from either the 3.8-litre V6, standard or supercharged, or a pair of 5.0 V8s. Holden's Special Vehicle Division produces a handsome range of enhanced V8s with the option of 5.7-litres.

Best All-Rounder: Commodore Acclaim V6

Body styles
Saloon, Estate
Engine capacity
3.8V6, 5.0V8, 5.7V8
Price from
Aus $30,000
Manufactured in
Australia

Commodore

honda

Honda

Honda's up-front technical prowess is unique amongst mainstream manufacturers. It has resulted in some extraordinarily powerful engines, not just in the NSX supercar but also cars ranging from the Civic to the Integra. Coupled with an envious reputation for quality, it should make Honda impossible to beat. But there are weaknesses as well, notably its interiors, which are functional but plain and rarely as roomy as their rivals. The range can be confusing too. The new Accord is built in three distinct versions in the UK, Japan and the States - Europe gets saloons from England but coupes from the US. There is a similar situation with the Civic. 1999 sees a new MPV, the Canadian-built MV99 and the Capa, which is similar in concept to the Mercedes-Benz A-Class.

Honda Accord

new!

This is the sixth generation of the Accord and the second to be tailored specifically for Europe. A touch shorter than before, new space-saving double wishbone rear suspension results in more room for passengers and luggage. In addition to the expected saloon, a hatchback version will be introduced in 1999.

Honda's undoubted grasp on technology has never quite resulted in past Accords being great cars, but the promise of this new model is strong if the suspension is as good as Honda claim. There are, of course, engines of great power, including a new 2.2-litre Type-R with 215bhp. Buyers can also choose a sophisticated sequential shift automatic transmission.

Best All-Rounder: Too early to tell

Body styles Saloon, Hatchback, Coupe
Engine capacity 1.8, 2.0, 2.2, 3.0V6
Price from £15,300
Manufactured in Japan, England, United States

S98 HON

Honda Shuttle/Odessy

For a while the Shuttle was the best selling car in Japan, but in the UK it has been mostly forgotten due to its high price and lack of versatility. Compared to other MPVs the Shuttle seems almost impractical with no removable rear seats, and the driving experience is dull but car-like.

Honda cut the Shuttle's price to try and make it more competitive, but it is the lack of choice which ultimately lets it down, Only a slow-shifting automatic gearbox is available linked to a thirsty 2.3-litre petrol engine. Two models are offered though, the entry-level LS with seven seats and the luxurious ES with six individual 'captain's chairs'.

Best All-Rounder: Shuttle 2.3i LS

Body styles
MPV

Engine capacity
2.2

Price from
£18,200

Manufactured in
US

Honda Civic

Honda's Escort-class competitor is a confusing range of machines that are only loosely related. The British-built five-door hatchback and estate are kissing cousins to Rover's 400 hatch. The saloon is derived from the Japanese-built three-door hatchback, both from a newer, sixth generation of Civic. So is the Coupe, but this is built in the States.

The Civic's appeal, however, runs across the range, with models to charm the mature driver looking for a reliable, refined cruiser matched to those who demand an understated performance machine. For the latter, smooth VTEC power is coupled with race-car like double-wishbone suspension, and it's this which allows near class leading refinement and pace.

Best All-Rounder: Civic 1.5 LSi 5dr

Body styles
Hatchback, Saloon, Coupe, Estate

Engine capacity
1.4, 1.5, 1.6, 1.8, 2.0TD

Price from
£12,500

Manufactured in
Japan, England, United States

Honda Legend

Honda has proved it can compete in most sectors, so it's a surprise that its attempt at taking on BMW's 5-Series has failed. You may wonder why - £34,000 seems reasonable for a car of the Legend's size loaded with every conceivable extra, but besides not being entertaining to drive, the Honda lacks the prestige badge so essential in this class.

There is only one Legend derivative available, powered by the 200bhp, 3.5-litre V6. There are few extras available as almost everything is standard, from leather upholstery to CD player. Honda's reliability is good too, but you are offered more choice, and a better drive, in other manufacturer's ranges.

Best All-Rounder: Legend 3.5 V6

Body styles
Saloon

Engine capacity
3.5V6

Price from
£34,100

Manufactured in
Japan

Honda Integra

The Integra appears in a number of forms throughout the world, the core models being a sleek four-door saloon and stylish two-door coupe. Engine power can be a 1.8-litre 16v unit producing a healthy 144bhp, but it is the scorching 1.8-litre Integra R which raises the game.

This is a staggering machine. A kitten to drive around town, it transforms into a tiger as the revs rise, the 190 bhp producing breathtaking acceleration. There is a great chassis and excellent steering to complement the performance, though this is a totally no compromise machine. Noise, fuel consumption and the ride are all horrifying.

Best All-Rounder: Integra Type-R

Body styles
Coupe, Saloon

Engine capacity
1.8

Price from
£19,800

Manufactured in
Japan

Honda NSX

The showcase for Honda's renowned engineering prowess, the NSX boasts an aluminium body and suspension and a 276bhp V6 24-valve engine with VTEC variable valve lift and variable induction. A six-speed gearbox is standard, but a semi-automatic is offered too. The coupe is complemented by the removable roof on the NSX-T version.

It is a stunning car to drive, with enormous depths to its performance and a sound like a muted Grand Prix car. Yet the NSX is child's play to drive around town, just like any other Honda. And that is its major weakness - the NSX just doesn't feel special enough inside for a car of its calibre and price.

Best All-Rounder: NSX Coupe

Body styles
Coupe, Targa

Engine capacity
3.0V6, 3.2V6

Price from
£69,600

Manufactured in
Japan

Honda Prelude

In its latest form the Prelude has changed direction a little. The styling is more conservative, but the interior space has improved. The result is mixed - the new car is dull in appearance, both inside and out, and while it is roomier it is still a tight fit for adults in the rear seats.

But the Prelude remains a great drive. Two engines are offered, a 2.0-litre and a higher performance 2.2 with Honda's VTEC and 185bhp. The latter is exceptional, howling enthusiastically to high revs whenever required. It comes with four-wheel steering as standard, with handling beyond reproach.

Best All-Rounder: Prelude 2.2 VTi

Body styles
Coupe

Engine capacity
2.0, 2.2

Price from
£19,100

Manufactured in
Japan

Honda CR-V

This compact 4x4 sector is expanding rapidly. The key is practicality and Honda's CR-V offers lots of thoughtful touches. The floor is completely flat, rather like an MPVs, and the seating positions can be changed. There's a concealed luggage area under the floor and the lid of this can be removed for use as a table.

The 2.0-litre engine gives performance which is usefully brisk, though it's hardly the GTi in 4x4 clothing that has made the Toyota RAV4 such a hit. Similarly, handling and ride are acceptable rather than inspiring. But it is a solid, roomy, well-built machine that is actually rather enjoyable to own and drive.

Best All-Rounder: CR-V 2.0 ES

Body styles
Estate

Engine capacity
2.0

Price from
£16,600

Manufactured in
Japan

Honda Logo

Honda's Logo is just one of the dozens of tiny town cars that prove popular in Japan yet rarely reach the export markets. Comparable with European cars like the Ka and Twingo, the newly developed 1.3-litre engine has been designed to provide a bigger punch at low to medium speeds, with the option of two types of automatic transmission plus a five-speed manual.

Available as both a three and five-door hatchback, the Logo is a straightforward small car with a reasonable amount of room inside but better than average practicality. The seats are relatively high, giving the driver increased visibility and those in the rear more foot room.

Best All-Rounder: Logo 1.3 Multi-Matic

Body styles
Hatchback

Engine capacity
1.3

Price from
£n.a.

Manufactured in
Japan

Isuzu

General Motors has a big stake in Isuzu, with the result that there is some muddying of the waters when it comes to the model range. Isuzu's big off-roader, the Trooper, is also sold in the UK as the Vauxhall Monterey and in Europe as an Opel. Ironically, despite the massive marketing power of GM, the Trooper heavily outsells the Monterey in Britain. The Vauxhall/Opel Frontera is also an Isuzu model, although this time vehicles for European consumption are built in the UK with no competition from Japan. In the States Isuzu also sells a range of small family cars.

Trooper

Isuzu Trooper

The Japanese marque's sole model in the UK continues to sell despite the appearance of an identical version badged as a Vauxhall Monterey. The Trooper has had a recent facelift to bring it nearer rivals, but the interior still looks dated and it is still not as competent on or off road.

The revamp brought two new engines, a refined but thirsty 3.5-litre V6 petrol and an impressive turbodiesel. The latter suits the Trooper better, with more low-down torque. The three door is better off-road, but the long wheelbase is more practical with a seven seat option. Citation models add useful equipment.

Body styles Estate **Engine capacity** 3.5V6, 3.0TD **Price from** £21,000 **Manufactured in** Japan

Vehicross

Off-roading moves straight into the next century with the VehiCross, and there is little that will draw more attention in the High Street. Except that it won't because little more than 10 a day are built, and they are all swallowed up by eager buyers in Japan.

Based upon the running gear of the Trooper, with a 212bhp V6 engine and sports suspension, the VehiCross goes and handles like no other off-roader - though it is probably worse than most in the rough stuff. Inside there's barely room for four, but that hardly matters in a sporting car, does it?

Vehicross

Body styles Estate **Engine capacity** 3.5V6 **Price from** £n.a. **Manufactured in** Japan

Hyundai

1998 saw a year of major launches for Hyundai - a first time entry into the small town-car market with the Atoz, a new and much improved Sonata large family saloon, and a facelifted Lantra. The company still struggles to design cars with the all-round accomplishment of the major European manufacturers, but it is increasingly getting there. To make up for it Hyundai offers great value-for-money packages, with highly competitive pricing and long-term warranties. Combined with its traditionally high levels of build quality and reliability, the Korean firm is definitely one to watch for the future.

Hyundai Sonata   *new!*

This new Hyundai is now firmly pitched against mainstream family rivals like the Mondeo, offering in the place of the familiarity of its mainstream rivals, an abundance of passenger space, heaps of equipment and a great warranty. The Sonata has just one body style - the saloon - and the choice of a 2.0-litre four cylinder engine, or a 2.5 V6 coupled to an automatic transmission.

It is the sort of car that does almost everything at least adequately, but stands out in no area. So the performance is OK, the comfort satisfactory and the refinement reasonable. The overall selling package - and the space - remain the outstanding features.

Best All-Rounder: Sonata 2.0 CDX

Body styles Saloon
Engine capacity 2.0, 3.0V6
Price from £14000
Manufactured in Korea

Hyundai Accent

Hyundai is hoping that soon enthusiasts will really ache for one of its cars. It is getting there with the Coupe, but the bread and butter models like the Accent gain sales largely by offering a lot of space for the money. The Accent may be Escort-sized, but it's Fiesta-priced.

The cheapest hatchbacks and 'coupes' come fairly miserably equipped, but move up through the range and you can have an air-conditioned 1.5-litre car for little more cost than an entry-level European. It's in the detailing that the price difference tells though - the cabins are full of cheap plastic switchgear and trim.

Best All-Rounder: Accent 1.3 LSi

Body styles
Hatchback, Saloon

Engine capacity
1.3, 1.5

Price from
£7,600

Manufactured in
Korea

Hyundai Lantra

A recent facelift has made the Lantra look competitive, with new external styling tweaks, improvements in engine refinement and a better quality interior. The basic value remains built into the car though, as it continues to offer a Ford Mondeo-sized family car for the price of a smaller Escort.

Both engine options, 1.6 or 2.0-litre petrol units, are smooth, powerful, and fuel economy is good for this size of car too. Equipment levels are high, and even the supermini-priced Si has electric windows and sunroof as standard. The estate makes a stylish and practical no-nonsense workhorse.

Best All-Rounder: Lantra 1.6 GLSi Estate

Body styles
Saloon, Estate

Engine capacity
1.6, 2.0

Price from
£10,600

Manufactured in
Korea

Hyundai Atoz   *new!*

The Koreans traditionally copy the Japanese, so it is no surprise to see Hyundai's 'high-roof' supermini in the style of the Daihatsu Move and Suzuki Wagon R. Neither car sells well in the conservative UK market, but Hyundai thinks acceptable dynamics and keen pricing will change people's views.

The Atoz uses a new, specially developed 1.0-litre engine which is both refined and economical. The high roof may look odd, but it means the interior is comfortable even for tall passengers. Both models have power steering as standard, while the posher Plus package adds air conditioning and electric windows.

Best All-Rounder: Atoz +

Body styles
Hatchback

Engine capacity
1.0

Price from
£7,000

Manufactured in
Korea

Hyundai Coupe

A car as beautiful as the Coupe is a sure sign the Koreans are now a force to be taken seriously. It is not just good to look at either, as the Lantra's fine 1.6 and 2.0-litre engines endow it with perky performance, and there is reasonable practicality. Only the interior quality doesn't stand comparison to rivals.

The bargain priced 1.6-litre model offers style and generous equipment for little more than the price of a supermini, but it is the 2.0-litre models which go as well as they look with an eager 137bhp engine. The top SE model looks pricey but is loaded with equipment.

Best All-Rounder: Coupe 2.0 SE

Body styles
Coupe

Engine capacity
1.6, 1.8, 2.0

Price from
£14,000

Manufactured in
Korea

jaguar

Jaguar

While it undoubtedly upset long-term enthusiasts, Ford ownership has turned Jaguar around. Renowned for its combination of sporting luxury coupled to keen pricing, Jaguar struggled to shake off quality problems for too many years. Today things are much, much better, and the future more exciting than ever. The XJ saloon now has V8 engines to rival those of BMW and Mercedes Benz. The XK8 coupe and convertible can handle the competition without any apologies. And then there is the new S-Type, bringing Jaguar into the reach of a wider population of car buyers, to be followed in a couple of years by the smaller X200 which will compete with the BMW 3-Series and Audi A4.

XK8 Convertible

Jaguar XK8

Offered in coupe or convertible forms, this 2+2 grand tourer has set the luxury car world alight, combining traditional Jaguar virtues with new standards of quality and with the sort of value that makes the competition - notably Mercedes-Benz - look absurdly over-priced.

At the heart of the XK8 is a 4.0-litre V8, either in standard or supercharged (XKR) form. Even the standard XK8 is a peach to drive, smooth yet with a high level of sporting accomplishment. The XKR is phenomenal, providing performance unmatched at the price. The detail work inside the XK8 is delightful, with plenty of leather, wood and thick carpeting giving it real class, and comfort for hours on end.

Best All-Rounder: XK8 Coupe

Body styles Coupe, Convertible
Engine capacity 4.0V8, 4.0V8 Supercharged
Price from £50,600
Manufactured in England

Jaguar XJ8

In the past, Jaguar's big saloons have 'enjoyed' a dubious reputation of, after a few years, becoming unreliable, unattractive and, well, cheap. The truth is that nowadays the XJ is a well-designed and well-built executive cruiser. Ford's money has gone towards making it almost the match of its German rivals.

Almost? Well, the sumptuously appointed cabin is tight on space, but maybe that makes it cosy. The boot isn't the best either, but perhaps that's how the XJ retains its sleek looks. Dynamically too, it lacks the poise of some BMWs – but then, grace is more important than lap times. As always, it's easy to make excuses for this most charismatic of executive saloons.

Best All-Rounder: XJ8 3.2

Body styles	Price from
Saloon	£36,400

Engine capacity	Manufactured in
3.2V8, 4.0V8, 4.0V8 Supercharged	England

Jaguar S-Type

Its name harks back to a time when Jaguars were more affordable, and this is the role the new S-Type has to fulfil - a cheaper range of cars designed to appeal to buyers of the BMW 5-Series. Ford's money has ensured major economies of scale, the most significant being that the S-type shares its platform design with the new American Lincoln LS.

There are engine similarities too, a V6 from Ford, the V8 from the current Jaguar range. But Jaguar's trump card will be its style. This computer rendition of how the car will look shows that character will be a major part of the Jaguar appeal from the outside, while inside expect the usual inimitable use of leather and wood.

Best All-Rounder: Too early to tell

Body styles	Price from
Saloon	£25,000 (est)

Engine capacity	Manufactured in
3.0V6, 3.2 V8	England

Kia

Kia is one of the smaller Korean car companies which looked healthy enough before the great recession hit its homeland. Now it is up for grabs with, perhaps surprisingly, a large number of strong suitors competing for it. This is a surprise, as this is no Rolls-Royce, just a manufacturer of ordinary family cars all of which are bettered by a large amount of the competition. Kia's latest car is the Credos, a Mondeo competitor that the UK, for one, has put on hold until the company's situation is more stable. Kia builds two hand-me-downs from other manufacturers - the Pride, a version of an earlier Mazda 121, and the Elan, from Lotus.

Kia Credos

Kia's biggest car is a viable-looking alternative to a Mondeo but, as with all of the marque's products, there is outdated technology lurking within. The Credos is based on the old model Mazda 626, which means it is dull to drive and unrefined compared to modern competition.

Two versions of the Credos will be available, using the 1.8-litre 16-valve engine with 116bhp from the Mentor, or the 133bhp 2.0-litre fitted to the Sportage. It was due to reach the UK later this year, but the financial problems in Korea have delayed its arrival. Prices are sure to be very keen.

Best All-Rounder: Too early to tell.

Body styles Saloon
Engine capacity 1.8, 2.0
Price from £n.a.
Manufactured in Korea

Kia Pride

Little more than a rebadged version of the long extinct Mazda 121 supermini, the Kia is way past its sell-by date. On paper it looks cheap and is surprisingly spacious inside, but it feels its age on the road. Build quality is reasonable, but the materials used feel cheap and look nasty.

Falling sales have whittled the Pride range to just one engine - the 1.3-litre - which needs to be worked hard despite the car's small dimensions. A five-door adds a little practicality for the family driver, and the LX throws in some essential options. The Pride's biggest problem however is that there are far better, younger rivals available for not much more money.

Best All-Rounder: Pride 1.3 LX 5dr

Body styles
Hatchback

Engine capacity
1.3

Price from
£6,200

Manufactured in
Korea

Kia Elan

Kia purchased the rights and the tools to make the Lotus Elan and now it is built in Korea. The original intention was to take advantage of lower costs for home and export markets, but Korea's and Kia's problems have slowed progress.

The engine is Kia's own 1.8-litre twin cam four-cylinder, but otherwise it is true to the original design. That means it drives just like the Lotus, great performance and handling that has to be experienced to be believed. But though Kia has done a good technical job, the interior needs a lot of attention and the price needs to be low - this is a ten year old design, after all.

Best All-Rounder: Elan 1.8

Body styles
Convertible

Engine capacity
1.8

Price from
£n.a.

Manufactured in
Korea

Kia Sportage

Kia's offering in the trendy sport off-roader market is more credible than its other models thanks to cheeky good looks and the fact it is built in Germany, not Korea. Inside there is a reasonable amount of room, and although the trim is not the best quality it should last well.

A 2.0-litre engine helps the Sportage perform reasonably on and off the road, but the car is let down by a choppy ride and lifeless steering on the tarmac and low ground clearance off it. All models are well equipped and it makes a viable alternative if you can't afford a Freelander. The UK only sees the five-door Sportage, although a three-door is available elsewhere.

Best All-Rounder: Sportage SLX

Body styles
Estate, Convertible

Engine capacity
2.0, 2.2D, 2.2TD

Price from
£14,400

Manufactured in
Korea, Germany

Kia Mentor

Escort-sized car, Fiesta-sized prices, but you have to be seriously disinterested in cars to want to own one of these. The interior is as bland as the exterior, but it makes up with extra standard equipment. The Mentor's refinement is way behind today's benchmarks, and its handling can catch out the inexperienced in emergencies.

Even the bargain-priced Start entry level model offers power steering as standard and is available at the same cost as a five-door hatchback or four-door saloon. In the UK all Mentors are powered by an unrefined but perky 1.5-litre engine. Top models are generously equipped and still reasonably priced.

Best All-Rounder: Mentor SLX 5dr

Body styles
Saloon, Hatchback

Engine capacity
1.5, 1.6, 1.8

Price from
£9,469

Manufactured in
Korea

Lada

Lada

Low-cost manufacturing has not been enough to keep Lada strong in export markets. The much-needed investment was just not available to develop its cars for the ever tougher regulations, so most of its production is now aimed at domestic buyers. So it is no longer possible to buy new versions of the decrepit Riva saloon and estate in the UK, nor the four-wheel-drive Niva. It's not much of a loss.

Niva

Lada Niva

One of the cheapest 4x4s on the market, the Niva sports little in the way of sophistication or refinements. Originally conceived for the Russian army, the Niva has a simple selectable four-wheel drive system which works pretty well off-road.

As a road car, the Niva remains pretty basic transport. Even with the later 1.7-litre engine with fuel injection, performance is modest in the extreme and there's no power steering to ease the high parking loads required. Inside, there's plenty of room for four hefty adults, but not much of a boot space behind the seats. Given a long enough straight, it will work its way noisily up to about 80mph. Show it a muddy track and the Niva feels far more confident.

Body styles Estate **Engine capacity** 1.7 **Price from** £n.a.
Manufactured in Russia

Samara

The Samara was Lada's 1980s attempt to produce a modern car; it failed miserably. About the only thing in its favour is price, and the fact that if you live in Russia, Ladas are the most readily available cars. Power is almost acceptable in 1.5 form, barely so with the 1.3 and lethargic in 1.1 guise. None is quiet, especially when worked hard, as each model needs to be. As expected, the chassis is soggy and ill-controlled; the equipment and safety spec minimal. Worst of all though, is the quality, a far cry from the standards currently achieved by Lada's one time rival, Skoda.

Samara

Body styles Hatchback, Saloon, Estate
Engine capacity 1.1, 1.5, 1.5 **Price from** £n.a. **Manufactured in** Russia

Lamborghini

Like Lotus, Lamborghini has a fabulous history of making sensational cars yet the financial footings of both companies have gone through bad times. In the summer of 1998 Lamborghini was bought by Audi and, it can be hoped, a settled time will be ahead for the Italian supercar manufacturer. It is too early to predict what effect this will have on the model range, save for the certainty that a new smaller and cheaper Lamborghini - to compete with the Ferrari F355 - will finally appear. As for the Diablo, it still thunders on - the last remaining mid-engined supercar in its price range from an almost forgotten era.

Lamborghini Diablo

That the Diablo still exists is probably down to it being the most outrageous supercars of them all. Its mid-mounted 5.7-litre V12 emits the most impossibly loud and thrilling bark, the wide-hipped, big-screened and waist-high looks guarantee it traffic-stopping attention in places where a modern breed of supercar, such as a Ferrari 550M, could pass unnoticed.

The 'standard' model will pull over 200mph. Although its cornering limits are extraordinarily high, at racetrack speeds the big mass of the V12 behind the driver can easily catch out the unskilled. The answer could be the VT model, with four-wheel-drive to keep things under more control. This transmission is shared with the open-topped Roadster. But the fastest, sharpest Diablo of them all is also the cheapest; the stripped-out SV is close to a race car in its sparseness and utilises the standard rear-wheel-drive layout and a 500bhp motor.

Best All-Rounder: Diablo SV

Body styles Coupe, Convertible **Engine capacity** 5.7 V12 **Price from** £135,500 **Manufactured in** Italy

Lancia

Distinguished, stylish but never excessive. That has been the Lancia credos since the company began in 1906, although the pressures of change have naturally had their effect on this manufacturer as all others. Today Lancia is part of the giant Fiat Group, mass produces its cars like any other maker, and has had to compromise its stance by producing cars like the "Y" supermini and the "Z" people-carrier which hardly fulfil the original brief. A fall in popularity forced Lancia to pull out of the right-hand-drive market some years ago.

Kappa Coupe

Lancia Kappa

Lancia's entry into the executive market does well in its home market of Italy, but few other markets can see its appeal. That's a shame because the distinctive slab-sided styling hides a competent car with tidy handling and great refinement. The coupe is weird looking, but the estate can offer luxury and space.

The Kappa will form the basis of the next big Alfa - the 166 - so it shares engines with the sporty marque, including the fabulous 3.0-litre V6. The 2.0-litre engines, even the turbo, are unrefined and sluggish, but the turbodiesel is a remarkably good all-rounder. While the station wagon is practical, the odd coupe is for enthusiasts only.
Best All-Rounder: Kappa 3.0 V6

Kappa Estate

Body styles Saloon, Coupe, Estate
Engine capacity 2.0, 2.0 Turbo, 2.4, 3.0V6, 2.5TD
Price from £n.a.
Manufactured in Italy

Lancia Dedra

When the Dedra was first launched, it wasn't just the name which failed to attract buyers. It had reasonable looks and some interesting engines, but the chassis was just not capable of matching the BMW 3-Series it was priced up against. Five years later, there have been few improvements but the competition has got even stiffer.

The range has now been cut down to just the 103bhp 1.6-litre and 130bhp 1.8-litre petrol engines or the 1.9-litre turbodiesel - not even the vaguely interesting and powerful turbo petrol engines remain. At least the station wagon is a reasonably stylish attempt at a load-carrier.

Best All-Rounder: Dedra 1.8 station wagon.

Body styles	**Price from**
Saloon, Estate	£n.a.
Engine capacity	**Manufactured in**
1.6, 1.8, 1.9TD	Italy

Lancia Y

Using the Fiat Punto's chassis, the Y was always going to be reasonable to drive, but Lancia has added a dash of style and luxury to the supermini class. The exterior's wacky styling is continued for the luxuriously-appointed interior, with centrally mounted instruments and suede-look trim for the seats and dashboard.

Three engine options are available, using the Punto's 1.2-litre engine in 60 bhp or 86bhp versions or the torquier 80bhp 1.4-litre from the Bravo. It's reasonably cheap in Italy too, but will never be engineered with right-hand drive. Its amazingly available in a choice of 112 different colours.

Best All-Rounder: Y 1.2 86bhp

Body styles	
Hatchback	
Engine capacity	
1.2, 1.4	
Price from	
£n.a.	
Manufactured in	
Italy	

Lancia Delta

Sharp looking and stylish, the Delta has never really managed to live up to the sporty brand image on the road, with dynamics which are way behind the class on the road and cramped interior packaging. Handling is way behind the class, with a lumpy ride and poor roadholding.

Available as a three or five door, the Delta is most convincing in HPE form with the 193bhp turbocharged 2.0-litre engine, and butch wider body work but the chassis still can't really cope. The lower-powered 1.6, 1.8 and 2.0-litre cars are well equipped and stylish inside but dull to drive.

Best All-Rounder: Delta HPE

Body styles	
Hatchback	
Engine capacity	
1.6, 1.8, 2.0, 2.0 Turbo	
Price from	
£n.a.	
Manufactured in	
Italy	

Land Rover

Easily the most successful arm of the Rover Group, Land Rover has the history and image that have carried it through good times and bad. Its recent success has been buoyed by the arrival of the Freelander, the new smaller Land Rover that answers the need of those that do not want a massive off-roader for town use. For 1999 the Discovery gets a major update to maintain its position against the competition, including a new five-cylinder turbo-diesel. The Range Rover also gets a revised 4.0-litre V8 with more power and torque, and the Defender - the original Land Rover - receives an update too.

Land Rover Freelander

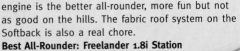

Smaller, cheaper and trendier than any previous Land Rover, the Freelander is another of the increasingly popular "lifestyle" 4x4s. Yet it is a credible off-roader, despite lacking the ground clearance of other Land Rovers. To compensate, there is a clever patented hill descent system that helps even novices tackle treacherous descents.

The Freelander is roomy and comfortable inside, and it drives more like a car than most 4x4s, though the gearchange is clunky. The turbo-diesel engine provides good performance, but it is too noisy except when cruising. The 1.8 petrol engine is the better all-rounder, more fun but not as good on the hills. The fabric roof system on the Softback is also a real chore.

Best All-Rounder: Freelander 1.8i Station Wagon

Body styles Estate, Convertible
Engine capacity 1.8, 2.5V6, 2.0TDi
Price from £16,600
Manufactured in England

Land Rover Discovery

new!

You have to hand it to Land Rover. It may hibernate a long time between new models, but every new launch it scores a resounding success. The original Discovery opened up the 4x4 market to those more interested in on-road comfort than climbing mountains, even though every Land Rover has impeccable credentials in that area too.

This heavily revised Discovery for 1999 has a lengthened body to make it into a genuine seven-seater, plus a heavily revised interior. Quality was not a high point with the old model, so great claims for improvement are made here too. The V8 engines are improved and there is a brand new five-cylinder turbo-diesel which should offer a necessary improvement in refinement.

Best All-Rounder: Discovery TDi

Body styles	Price from
Estate	£22,000

Engine capacity	Manufactured in
4.0V8, 2.5TDi	England

Land Rover Range Rover

The Range Rover stands apart from the common off-roader. Its opulence, equipment and, of course, its massive price, mean that it is more at home competing with luxury saloons. At least that is what Land Rover hopes, and the tactic comes off. The interior has the ambience and comfort of a Jaguar, with ample stretching-out space for passengers and luggage.

And of course, there is the outstanding off-road ability, with the Range Rover every bit as good as any other Land Rover. And as for the Range Rover cachet - how can a Nissan or Toyota hope to compete with that?

Best All-Rounder: Range Rover 4.0

Body styles
Estate

Engine capacity
2.5TD, 4.0V8, 4.6V8

Price from
£39,000

Manufactured in
England

Land Rover Defender

The Land Rover Defender is one of a tiny group of vehicles to reach immortality. Like the Mini and VW Beetle, it has remained a definitive model despite the attempts of others to oust it. Key to its success is the tough, rugged, no-nonsense design. Available in two basic forms, with either a 90 or 110 inch wheelbase, dozens of derivatives have been developed from this basic steel girder chassis/ aluminium panelled platform.

Perhaps the most unlikely derivative is the "civilised" County, which just goes to show that even the Defender has its limits. Best to think of it as a workhorse, and by picking the turbo-diesel, there is still little to better it.

Best All-Rounder: Defender TDi

Body styles
Estate, convertible

Engine capacity
2.5Tdi, 3.0V8

Price from
£17,000

Manufactured in
England

Lexus

Japanese car manufacturers have historically been very successful in all areas but one, exporting luxury cars. The problem is clear - buyers looking to spend case-fulls of money want a Mercedes-Benz, Jaguar, Cadillac or BMW. A Nissan or a Toyota just will not do no matter how good it is. So ten years ago Toyota came up with the Lexus idea, a brand new marque that produced only luxury cars. Starting with just a single model, the LS400 showed that it was possible for a Japanese manufacturer to produce a car to compete at the top end. Next up was the smaller GS300, a BMW 5-Series competitor. Some markets also see the stylish SC 300/400 coupe and there is an off-roader which competes head-to-head with the new Mercedes-Benz M-Class, the Lexus RX300.

Lexus IS200 *new!*

The exciting new IS200 is the smallest Lexus yet. Aimed directly at the new 3-Series BMW, the IS200 is a much more sporty proposition than any other Lexus, and the first to have a (six-speed) manual gearbox. Power comes from a new 2.0-litre, six-cylinder, 24-valve engine producing 165bhp, with the option, for those that want it, of a four-speed electronically controlled automatic transmission. A highly stylised car, the interior is said to take its cues from sports watches. Prices will be in the region of £22,000.

Body styles Saloon
Engine capacity 2.0
Priced from £22,000
Manufactured in Japan

Lexus GS300

The latest Lexus GS300 is a much more stylish competitor for the BMW 5-Series and Mercedes E-Class than before. Straight line performance is impressive without being outstanding, helped by an all-new five-speed automatic gearbox. Inside, there are a few too many hints at the car's Toyota parentage, but the cabin is ergonomically sound and flawlessly built.

On the road, the big Lexus feels solid and assured, with well-weighted steering and precise handling. The GS300 is hardly a sports saloon, but the quality and equipment make it an attractive proposition for those more interested in finer things.

Best All-Rounder: GS300 SE

Body styles	Price from
Saloon	£31,200

Engine capacity	Manufactured in
3.0	Japan

Lexus LS400

Toyota's first real attempt to topple the might of the European prestige manufacturers is a mighty impressive effort, especially in this revised form. The LS400 is more refined inside than a Rolls Royce, with a whisper quiet 4.0-litre V8 matched to the smoothest-shifting automatic gearbox in the world.

The revisions to the range have made the one LS400 model even more comfortable, and there is enough standard equipment to make a Mercedes owner weep. Even satellite navigation is standard - a first for a production car in the UK. Only the looks and the lack of a prestige badge prevent more sales.

Best All-Rounder: LS400

Body styles	Price from
Saloon	£50,000

Engine capacity	Manufactured in
4.0V8	Japan

Lincoln

Outside of the US, the only Lincoln people tend to remember is the Lincoln Continental John F. Kennedy was riding in the day he was assassinated. That could soon change. Next year, Ford's luxury car division, starts producing its LS saloon, based on the platform of the new Jaguar S-Type, which will also be available in Europe. This will be followed by a Lincoln version of the upcoming 'small' Jaguar that will rival BMW's 5-Series. This too will be sold in Europe. Back in the US, Lincoln sells an older audience. Models like the new Town Car, the Continental and Grand Marquis go to buyers who tend to want comfort rather than speed.

Lincoln Town Car

Car of choice for America's country club set, the XXL-sized Town Car is the last of the great rear-drive luxury-liners. Last year's radical re-design transformed the previous box-like six-seater into a svelte, swoopy thoroughbred. The sumptuous leather interior is almost decadent in its levels of comfort and luxury.

Previous Town Cars used to roll around like a freighter in a Force Five but not this one. Air suspension keeps the car horizontal on corners, and the variable-assist steering - while still light to the touch - has precision and feel. The multivalve 4.6-litre V8 could do with more power, but performance is far from shabby. A class act.

Best All-Rounder: Town Car Executive

Body styles
Saloon
Engine capacity
4.6V8
Price from
$38,000
Manufactured in
United States

Lincoln Continental

A little bit of Jaguar went into the recent re-design of Lincoln's luxury cruiser. In fact, the new rear lights and chrome accents around the boot could almost have been sourced from the XJ8. Re-designed interior trades American glitz for European glam, with its classy mix of soft leather and polished wood.

V8 muscle, in the form of Ford's formidable 4.6-litre, 260bhp 32-valver, provides the Continental with muscular performance and whisper-quiet cruising. Electronic wizardry gives the driver the choice of firm, normal or plush suspension settings, along with three choices of steering weight. For its bulk, the Continental is an accomplished handler.

Best All-Rounder: Continental V8

Body styles	Price from
Saloon	$38,000
Engine capacity	**Manufactured in**
4.6V8	United States

Lincoln Navigator

The unexpected US sales sensation of the year. Americans, who previously bought luxury saloons, are jumping on the sport-utility bandwagon and snapping-up over-sized 4x4s like the Navigator. Everything about this Lincoln is gargantuan; from its whale-like body, to its 5.4-litre V8. It comes with a sophisticated four-wheel drive system but few owners ever use it.

It may look rugged, but the Navigator offers every possible luxury; from leather trim and six-disc CD changer, to chrome wheels and deep-pile carpet. It also drives surprisingly well, with lively performance and safe, secure handling. It'll also carry seven passengers in comfort, while towing a small battleship behind.

Best All-Rounder: Navigator 4wd

Body styles
Estate

Engine capacity
5.4V8

Price from
$39,000

Manufactured in
United States

Lincoln LS *new!*

Lincoln goes global next year with the introduction of its new LS luxury saloon. Using the same platform as Jaguar's new S-Type, the LS will be sold in 30 countries around the world. It'll go head-to-head with the likes of Audi's A6, the Lexus GS300 and Cadillac's new Seville.

Lincoln has played a little too safe with the styling of the new LS; it's sort of Mitsubishi meets Mazda. But the Jaguar-developed underpinnings should ensure that the LS is a fine driver's car. Power will come from either Ford's 190bhp 3.0-litre V6, or an all-new 3.9-litre V8 developing 243bhp, mated to a five-speed automatic.

Best All-Rounder: Lincoln LS V6

Body styles
Saloon

Engine capacity
3.0V6, 3.9V8

Price from
$29,000

Manufactured in
United States

Lotus

Britain's pre-eminent sports car maker has gone through some tough times in the past, while the future do not look particularly rosy either. Problems in the Far East means that Lotus owner Proton is finding it increasingly difficult to find the cash to invest in the Norfolk company. For some time the majority of Lotus's income has come from consultancy work for other car manufacturers, but the production of the Elise has seen a turn around in car sales. As an example of advanced design and manufacturing techniques the Elise takes some beating - as it does on the road. But more investment is needed to produce a larger machine - the Esprit is looking decidedly long in the tooth.

Elise

Lotus Elise

Technically one of the most fascinating cars you can buy, the Elise makes use of an aluminium chassis weighing just 70kg, with brakes of aluminium composite. The driver's seat is mounted close to the centre line of the car to improve weight distribution. Power is provided by Rover's MGF engine mounted behind the seats.

The Elise is a car of little compromise. Driven hard there's little to equal it. The low weight ensures rapid acceleration, while the stability at speed, steering precision and handling are exemplary. But at other times it can be a real pain - unpleasantly noisy, long, notchy gearchange, suspension that crashes on bumps and a fiddly fabric roof.

Body styles Convertible **Engine capacity** 1.8 **Price from** £21,900 **Manufactured in** England

Lotus Esprit

The fundamental structure of the Esprit - mid-engined two-seater with turbocharged engines - remains true to the original of 22 years ago, but there have been many changes, notably a new body in 1987, V8 engine in 1997 and new interior in 1998.

The twin turbo-charged V8, producing 350bhp, ensures that the Esprit stays up there with the best supercars, and in true Lotus tradition, the steering and handling are perfectly matched to the performance. But it is a tough car to drive - the heavy clutch and gearchange and poor visibility confine the pleasure to open roads.

Body styles
Coupe
Engine capacity
2.0 turbo,
3.5V8 twin-turbo
Price from
£40,000
Manufactured in
England

Esprit

marcos

Marcos

Though Marcos has built many cars since the 1950's, they can be distilled down to just a handful of models. From the strange gull-wing sports cars of the 1950s, odd-looking but successful on the race track, to the current Mantis and MantaRay, there are just two or three really significant models in-between. The Mini Marcos was a successful attempt at taking the basics of a Mini and blending them into a tiny swooping coupe. It proved very popular with home builders. The Mantis name originally appeared both on a stunning racing car, complete with BRM Formula One engine, and also as a gawkish 2+2 which barely took off. But most important of all is the coupe. This car was designed by Dennis Adams and intriguingly used a chassis constructed of marine plywood. Today's cars bear a very strong family resemblance to that original car although that similarity and the use of glass-fibre reinforced plastic for the bodywork, is all that remains of the original.

Marcos MantaRay, LM and Mantis

The 1999 Marcos range consists of three models. New for 1999 is the MantaRay, replacing both the Mantara and the GTS, with a choice of V8 engines and Rover's impressive 2.0-litre turbo. The LM is a development of the Marcos racers with the full steroid treatment. Both are available as a fixed-head coupe or a convertible with a meaty large-capacity V8. The Mantis takes a 352bhp 4.6-litre US Ford V8 in an outrageously pumped-up version of the convertible. Performance of even the cheapest Marcos is breathtaking, but the Mantis is extraordinarily fast. All have a well-developed chassis and classy leather and Wilton interior.

Body styles
Coupe, Convertible
Engine capacity
2.0, 2.0 turbo, 4.0V8, 4.6V8, 5.0V8
Price from
£28,000
Manufactured in
England

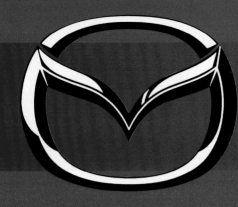

mazda

Mazda

Mazda produces a full range of family cars, yet it is the MX-5 sports car that readily comes to mind when the name is mentioned. The MX-5 has been a huge world-wide success, single-handedly responsible for the upsurge in new sports cars in the past three years. Now there is a new model which helps Mazda remain up there with the best. Otherwise the Mazda range is middle of the road - competent and well-developed but hardly exciting. Even the Xedos range of BMW competitors has never taken off in the way Mazda might have hoped. For 1999 there is a new 323 range and a facelift for the Xedos 9. The 121, a Fiesta clone built by Ford, sells fewer than 1% of the Ford in the UK and may be dropped.

Mazda 626

What is there to say about the latest Mazda 626, which replaced its worthy, bland predecessor in 1997? The new model offers a bit more space, a bit more refinement, a bit more equipment and a bit more economy for a bit less cost. That about sums it up.

The Mazda 626 is the motoring equivalent of easy listening. It offers none of the flair of a Passat, 406 or Mondeo. The cabin is efficient and fuss free, space all-round is more than class competitive and the equipment is generous. It seriously undercuts many of its rivals too. And to drive? As painless as you'd expect.

Best All-Rounder: 626 2.0 GXi

Body styles Hatchback, Saloon, Estate
Engine capacity 1.8, 2.0, 2.0TD
Price from £14,000
Manufactured in Japan

MAZ 1047

Mazda 121

There is a good reason for this Mazda to bear a resemblance to the Ford Fiesta - they are basically the same car, built on the same production line at Ford's Dagenham factory. Like Ford's supermini the Mazda is an appealing car to drive, boasting taut handling and a pleasantly refined ride, allied to lively performance. Power is provided by the impressive 1.25-litre Zetec SE engine, as well as the older but still capable Ford 1.3 unit.

This was never going to one of the roomiest superminis, but the 121 offers a fair amount of space for those in the front, with good comfort levels. Its weak points are in the accommodation for rear passengers and luggage.

Best All-Rounder 121 1.25-16v GSi

Body styles	Price from
Hatchback	£7,800

Engine capacity	Manufactured in
1.3, 1.25, 1.4, 1.8D	England

Mazda Demio

The Demio is intended to provide the space of a family car with the economy of a supermini. Its interior is certainly versatile, with a high driving position giving good visibility and rear seats that slide fore and aft to improve either legroom or luggage space. There's not a lot of headroom in the rear though.

The 1.3-litre unit seems perky around town, but it's unwilling on the open road. The steering and controls are light and easy-to-use, but the Demio doesn't have the fun-to-drive factor of a Fiesta or Polo. It's a brave attempt to be different without being plain silly, but a conventional supermini still has more appeal.

Best All-Rounder: Demio 1.3

Body styles
Estate

Engine capacity
1.3, 1.5

Price from
£10,500

Manufactured in
Japan

Mazda 323   *new!*

Mazda's Escort-sized 323 is re-launched for 1999 in a roomier format, although with much the same exterior dimensions. As before, there are three body styles, and again, Mazda has produced a rather muddled answer to its requirements. The five-door hatchback - easily the most popular model in the UK - is all-new, and there is a four-door saloon derived from this. The three-door hatch, on the other hand, is a carry-over from the previous range.

Petrol engines are re-worked versions of the existing power units in 1.3, 1.5 and 1.8-litre capacity, but there will also be the turbo-diesel from the 626 with a touch less power.

Best All-Rounder: Too early to tell

Body styles
Hatchback, Saloon

Engine capacity
1.3, 1.5, 1.8, 2.0TD

Price from
£14,500

Manufactured in
Japan

Mazda Xedos 6

Mazda has tried to muscle in on the hot sector dominated by strong competitors such as the BMW 3-Series and Audi A4, largely without success. This is a great shame, as the Xedos 6 is well built, refined and its silky smooth V6 engine performs well. Oddly for a Japanese car, even the styling is eye-catching and distinctive.

The main bugbear of the small Xedos is the cramped interior, with the rear cabin especially tight for all but the smallest adults. As you would expect, even the entry V6 is equipped well, but the SE adds leather and air conditioning. All that's missing is a classy badge.

Best All-Rounder: Xedos 6 2.0 SE

Body styles	**Price from**
Saloon	£22,000
Engine capacity	**Manufactured in**
1.6, 2.0V6	Japan

Mazda Xedos 9

Low sleek and good looking, the Xedos 9 is beautifully finished inside and out. The interior feels solid and classy, with ruched leather on the seats, matching inserts in the doors and a nicely 'hewn' look to the facia. Room in the rear is adequate, no more, but seat comfort is high.

1999 sees the addition of a super-charged Miller-cycle engine which is claimed to offer greater efficiency. The Xedos 9 needed more power to keep up with competition, so this may be the answer, although the engine and automatic transmission have always been ultra-smooth. The steering and suspension also need refining, if the Xedos 9 is to tempt BMW 5-Series drivers.

Best All-Rounder: Too early to tell

Body styles
Saloon

Engine capacity
2.5V6

Price from
£29,000

Manufactured in
Japan

Mazda MX-5

Eight years at the top is a long time for any car, yet Mazda sold more MX-5s in 1997 than in any previous year. Consequently it wisely exercised caution when altering a near-legend, carrying over many parts and re-engineering rather than replacing.

The new MX-5 is an even better driver's car as a result: the chassis is exploitable, the steering is fabulous and the switch-like gearbox is the best in the business. The engines have had a mild re-work to up their power and, like the interior, they're adequate rather than spectacular, but overall the new MX-5 is one of the best drives around.

Best All-Rounder: MX-5 1.8

Body styles
Convertible

Engine capacity
1.6, 1.8

Price from
£15,500

Manufactured in
Japan

Maserati

The company with a name to die for has had little else to shout about for far too long. Its Bi-Turbo models and endless derivatives were certainly fast enough, but lacked the charisma of those earlier Maseratis, with levels of quality that had hardly moved out of the 1970s. Today the company is owned by Fiat and in future its luxury sporting coupe and saloon are to be sold at prices mid-way between an executive car and a Ferrari.

Quattroporte

Maserati Coupe   *new!*

Forget the troubled build quality and dated dynamics which have blighted Maserati. Now Ferrari is in control and has promised to make this coupe a true rival to Jaguar and Aston Martin. If the performance and quality are right this could be the car to put the marque back up with the greats.

The all-new Maserati will go as well as it looks. Power is from a twin-turbocharged 3.2-litre V8 producing around 370bhp. Ferrari engineers will ensure it handles too, helped by traction control and electronic suspension. Prices will closely match the Jaguar XK8 at around £60,000 when it reaches the UK in spring 1999.

Maserati Quattroporte

There isn't much demand for Italian family four-door saloons which have supercar performance, which explains why you don't see many Quattroportes around. Powerful twin-turbo V6 and V8 engines delight and thrill but limited rear seat room, tricky rear-drive handling and suspect build quality make this a choice for the dedicated enthusiast only.

Available with either a 284bhp engine or an even more entertaining 335bhp V8, the four-door Maserati may be the answer for those wanting to please the family and satisfy their lust for exotic Italian sportscars. The trouble for Maserati is there are better built and equally rapid saloons from Jaguar and Mercedes.

Maserati Coupe

Body styles
Coupe: Coupe; Quattroporte: Saloon
Engine capacity
All with twin-turbos
Coupe: 3.2V8;
Quattroporte:
2.0V6, 2.8V6,
3.2V8
Price from
Coupe:
£50,00
(est);
Quattroporte:
£50,000
Manufactured in
Italy

Mercedes-Benz

The progress of development at Mercedes-Benz continues to run at breakneck speed. The company seems to have survived the debacle surrounding the instability of early versions of the A-Class and is now pressing ahead with the replacement for the S-Class luxury saloon. The coupe version, the CL, continues in the current form, based around the 1998 and earlier S-Class. Also hitting the showrooms during 1998 were the stylish four-seater convertible version of the CLK and the US-built M-Class off-roader, which launches in the UK at a very competitive price of £32,000.

Mercedes A-Class

Mercedes thought it had re-invented the Mini with a car shorter than a supermini and as spacious and safe as a family saloon, but after that infamous cornering manoeuvre it was forced back to the drawing board with a red face. The flexible seating positions and revolutionary packaging are still inspired though.

The revised car has tweaked suspension and a host of electronic devices to keep it on its wheels, but it now has a far harsher ride than the competition. The all new engines and gearboxes, especially the diesel, are efficient, but it still looks pricey. That badge will be enough to convince some buyers though.

Best All-Rounder: A170 turbodiesel

Body styles Hatchback
Engine capacity 1.4, 1.6, 1.7TD
Price from £14,490
Manufactured in Germany

Mercedes C-Class

Despite a recent facelift Mercedes' best-seller looks and feels old next to its rivals, but it still appeals to buyers who appreciate top-class levels of finish and safety. High prices and sparse equipment are offset by top quality, durability and excellent residuals.

The range of saloons and estates now includes four, six and eight-cylinder petrol engines and two refined and economical turbodiesels. All are long distance cruisers rather than sports cars, and even the awesome 306bhp C43 AMG is more at home on the autobahn than backroad. It's not inspiring, but offers all the good-points of a Mercedes in a compact package.

Best All-Rounder: C240 saloon

Body styles
Saloon, Estate

Engine capacity
1.8, 2.0, 2.3K, 2.4, 2.8, 3.6, 2.2D, 2.2TD, 2.5TD

Price from
£20,000

Manufactured in
Germany

Mercedes E-Class

The bug-eyed four-headlamp look of the E-Class caused controversy when the car first appeared, but now the buying public can look past it and see a fine car which is all a Mercedes is expected to be. The build quality is typically excellent and it is noticeably more roomy inside than rivals from BMW and Jaguar.

It may not be as exciting to drive as rivals, but the E-Class still impresses on the road thanks to a range of new V6 engines, or refined and economical turbodiesels. The flagship V8-engined AMG E55 is a real four-door supercar, and the estate cars make practical and refined load-carriers.

Best All-Rounder: E280 saloon.

Body styles
Saloon, Estate

Engine capacity
2.0, 2.4, 2.8, 3.2, 4.2V8, 5.0V8, 2.2D, 2.5TD, 3.2TD

Price from
£26,300

Manufactured in
Germany

Mercedes S-Class/CL Coupe

Having been beaten to Rolls-Royce by BMW and Volkswagen, Mercedes hopes to go one better with its new Maybach luxury saloon, but it will be tough to better the forthcoming new S-Class.

The luxury saloon is shorter than its predecessor and with softer styling but Mercedes will be hoping that once again it will set the standards for every other luxury saloon to match both technically and dynamically. Initial engine choice will range from a 2.8 V6 up to a 5.0-litre V8 with a V12 due in early 2000 and a turbodiesel engine also due next year. The present CL Coupe will continue to be offered for the time being, before being replaced late in 1999.

Best All-Rounder: Too early to tell

Body styles
Saloon, Coupe

Engine capacity
2.8, 3.2, 4.2V8, 5.0V8

Price from
£45,000 (est)

Manufactured in
Germany

Mercedes SLK

Following the huge publicity that surrounded its launch, life has settled down for the SLK, relatively speaking anyway. Although still boasting a huge waiting list, the premium market is slowly dwindling as more and more SLKs are seen on the road.

Nevertheless, the baby Mercedes still has that clever electric steel roof that folds away into the boot and the 2.3-litre supercharged engine offers a fair level of refinement. A 2.0-litre model is also available outside the UK. However, when al-fresco the roof steals boot space, performance is rather lacklustre thanks in part to a standard auto gearbox and there are some appalling optional colour schemes.

Best All-Rounder: SLK 230K

Body styles
Convertible

Engine capacity
2.0, 2.0K, 2.3K

Price from
£31,600

Manufactured in
Germany

Mercedes CLK

In a similar scenario to that seen with the smaller SLK, the initial publicity surrounding the Mercedes CLK coupe (and indeed its Cabriolet stablemate) has tended to centre on its huge popularity. In short, if you want one, you'd better not be in a hurry or be prepared to pay a premium over the list price.

Although based on the C-Class, the CLK borrows the bug-eyed look of the larger E-Class and has a choice of three engines - 2.0, supercharged 2.3 or a 3.2-litre V6. Each is available in Elegance or Sport trim and an automatic gearbox is a must (it's standard on the V6 models). Otherwise, the CLK offers reasonable accommodation considering it's a coupe and a substantial boot if a rather sanitised driving experience.

Best All-Rounder: CLK 230K

Body styles
Coupe, Convertible

Engine capacity
2.0, 2.0T, 2.3K, 3.2V6

Price from
£27,400

Manufactured in
Germany

Mercedes SL

It may no longer be the newest kid on the block and it may have had its halo stolen by the likes of the SLK and CLK, but the Mercedes SL remains the convertible at the top of most people's wish-lists.

With a removable hard-top making the SL effectively a coupe for the winter months, it is available with a range of engines from 2.8 up to a whopping 6.0-litre V12. A 6.0-litre V8-engined AMG version is also on offer. It does not have the SLK's trick hood, but the SL's fully-electric folding canvas offering is still a head-turner and a wonder of modern engineering. The SL is in its autumn years, hence comes loaded with standard equipment to maintain interest.

Best All-Rounder: SL320

Body styles
Convertible

Engine capacity
2.8, 3.2, 5.0V8, 6.0V12

Price from
£58,300

Manufactured in
Germany

Mercedes V-Class

People-carriers are often derided as being nothing more than vans with windows and in this case they're right - the Mercedes V-Class is based on the Vito van and it shows.

The upside of that is the huge amount of interior space with six comfortable captain's chairs and sliding rear doors for easier access to the rear. The downside is that the V-Class is thirsty and uncompromising on the road due to its van roots. It is offered with the choice of a 2.3 or 2.8-litre petrol, although others are in the pipeline. Coupled to average equipment levels and a high list price, more mainstream MPVs make better sense.

Best All-Rounder: V230

Body styles
MPV

Engine capacity
2.3, 2.8

Price from
£22,400

Manufactured in
Spain

Mercedes M-Class   *new!*

Mercedes would probably rather forget the angular G-Wagen off-roader that it produced primarily for the German army and concentrate on the new M-Class as an advert for its mud-plugging exploits.

Tuned specifically for on-road driving, the M-Class may beat its rivals on the tarmac but it will be hard pushed to match the likes of the Range Rover when the going gets muddier. To begin with, it will be available with 3.2 V6 and 3.4-litre V8 engines, although other powerplants will follow in due course. More concerning is the fact that some early cars have suggested that quality control standards at the M-Class's new US-plant are not up to usual Mercedes levels...

Best All-Rounder: Too early to tell

Body styles
Estate

Engine capacity
3.2V6, 3.4V8

Price from
£31,800

Manufactured in
United States

MCC Smart

It seems like a logical idea. Most cars have only one or two occupants, so why not develop a small car with just two seats? Mercedes-Benz and Swatch joined forces in 1994 to start the Micro Compact Car company. The Smart should have been on sale in Spring 1998 but worries over stability, following the Mercedes A-Class debacle, have pushed the date back.

Buyers can choose from three engines - petrol, diesel and a hybrid - and the modular body means that the Smart can be freshened up with a new set of body panels. Crucially, though it must be cheap to succeed. Will it?

Best All-Rounder: Too early to tell

Body styles	Price from
Hatchback	£6,000 (est)

Engine capacity	Manufactured in
600	France

Mercury Grand Marquis

Ford's Mercury Grand Marquis is as American as Howdy-Doody, Dolly Parton and mom's apple pie. It's one of the few surviving six-passenger, body-on-frame construction, rear-drive, V8-powered four-doors left. Costing the equivalent of just £14,000, it is staggeringly good value and last year's face-lift only widened its appeal.

The Grand Marquis earns its stripes as an impressive grand tourer. Solid, straight-line performance, whisper-quiet cruising, and a relaxed ride make 800-mile journeys a breeze in this cavernous four-door. Don't expect to push the handling envelope, but the re-designed steering and suspension combine to give safe, secure road manners.

Best All-Rounder: Grand Marquis LS

Body styles	Price from
Saloon	$22,000

Engine capacity	Manufactured in
4.6V8	United States

Mitsubishi

Mitsubishi

For some time it has been all too easy to associate Mitsubishi with just one model - the hugely successful Shogun off-roader. It is a vehicle with worldwide appeal and as a result has become a mainstay of the range. But Mitsubishi also has a wide choice of passenger cars, and now it is the Carisma, built in Holland alongside the Volvo S40 and aggressively priced, that has been responsible for a major growth in sales making it the best selling Mitsubishi in many European markets. There are major new models for 1999 too - replacements for the Space Wagon and Space Runner, a new European-built Space Star and a cheaper off-roader, the Challenger.

Mitsubishi Carisma

The Mitsubishi Carisma and Volvo S40 are built on the same production line in Holland. But while the Volvo is a stylish alternative to a BMW 3-Series, the Carisma is only stylish if compared to cars of the 1970s. It is, however, pitched further downmarket than the S40.

The range starts off at little more than the price of a small-medium sector car, so the Carisma can really score in terms of space. And its GDi petrol engine is one of the technological developments of the decade. If only the ride, handling and (predictably) charisma showed more promise, it could compete more than on price and that engine.

Best All-Rounder: Carisma 1.8 GDi

Body styles Saloon, Hatchback
Engine capacity 1.6, 1.8, 1.9 TDi
Price from £12,400
Manufactured in Netherlands

Mitsubishi Colt

The Mitsubishi Colt may draw plenty of admirers for its unusual looks, but it has a limited appeal with only one bodystyle - a three-door hatchback.

However, the Colt still manages to find customers who value ease of driving and peace of mind with Mitsubishi's extensive warranty package, despite the cramped interior and lack of character compared with rivals. The two engines on offer, a 1.3 and 1.6, are both refined and smooth and build quality is second to none. With a hefty price tag though, better value can be found in other superminis.

Best All-Rounder: Colt 1.3 GLX

Body styles
Hatchback

Engine capacity
1.3, 1.5, 1.6, 1.8, 2.0 turbo, 2.0TD

Price from
£10.800

Manufactured in
Japan

Mitsubishi Galant

The latest Galant, available as a saloon or estate with 2.0-litre four cylinder or 2.5 V6 engines, can lay a strong claim to being Mitsubishi's best car yet. By any standards this is a fine-looking car which sits at ease alongside its more expensive rivals. Comfort is good, the front seats are supportive, equipment is generous and there is a decent amount of room.

Given that the engines are only modestly powerful, the smooth and constant power delivery and sparkling performance is all the more impressive. Refinement is excellent too. The Galant is a great choice for those prepared to step out of line.

Best All-Rounder: Galant V6

Body styles
Saloon, estate

Engine capacity
1.8, 2.0, 2.0V6, 2.5V6, 2.0TD

Price from
£17.500

Manufactured in
Japan

Mitsubishi 3000GT

As a showcase for automotive technology, the 3000GT is undeniably impressive. Four-wheel-drive, active speed-sensitive spoilers, a twin-turbo 24-valve V6 engine and six-speed gearbox all feature in this big, brash GT. They all work efficiently and the car is endowed with huge reserves of performance, grip and traction. On a wet road it will leave many a pure sports car a long way behind.

Yet there are those that criticise the 3000GT precisely because it is so competent, complaining that the challenge and excitement of driving a high performance car is lost. Perhaps it is too big and heavy to be a truly sporting machine - but as a GT it excels.

Best All-Rounder: 3000 GT

Body styles
Coupe

Engine capacity
3.0V6, 3.0V6 turbo

Price from
£45,800

Manufactured in
Japan

Mitsubishi Space Wagon and Runner *new!*

The Mitsubishi Space Wagon was one of the first cars purpose-designed to carry seven people. 1999 sees the third-generation model appear, once more a vehicle that is smaller and more wieldy than the 'big-bus' mainstream competition. That compact size has its appeal, though the pricing needs to be lower too, something Mitsubishi has struggled with in the past.

The Wagon gets a new super-economical 2.4-litre GDi petrol engine. The five-seat Space Runner has the 1.8-litre equivalent from the Carisma. It is basically a shortened version of the Wagon and is intended more as a life-style vehicle, with removable seats and a sexier front end design.

Best All-Rounder: Space Wagon 2.4 GDi

Body styles
MPV

Engine capacity
1.8, 2.0 turbo, 2.4

Price from
Wagon: £16,500 (est)
Runner: £14,500 (est)

Manufactured in
Japan

Mitsubishi Space Star

new!

The Space Star is Mitsubishi's contribution to the class established by the Renault Scenic. A five-door cross between a hatchback and an estate, it combines compact exterior dimensions with a versatile and roomy interior. Like the Scenic, the body is tall, which allows passengers to sit upright and frees up room for luggage. Initially there will be two engines, a 1.8 GDi and a 1.3.

The Space Star is built alongside the Carisma and Volvo S40 in the jointly owned factory in the Netherlands. The question is, while most manufacturers are coming up with a car like this, has Mitsubishi one too many Space vehicles in its line up?

Best All-Rounder: Space Star 1.8 GDi

Body styles	Price from
MPV	£12,000

Engine capacity	Manufactured in
1.3, 1.8	Holland

Mitsubishi Shogun

One of most popular 4x4s in the world, the Shogun has acquired its reputation through extreme toughness and durability off-road. There's a choice of short-wheelbase three-door body or long-wheelbase five-door, as well as two tough turbo-diesels and two powerful petrol V6s.

As a road-going car it is less successful. The interior packaging is far from perfect, lacking the space or comfort of cheaper MPV's, despite seven seats in the five-door model. And it is questionable whether the myriad of adjustments available - seat springing, suspension softness, rear heating and so on - are of real value or merely covering up indifferent design.

Best All-Rounder: Shogun 2.8 TD GLX 5dr

Body styles
Estate

Engine capacity
2.4, 3.0V6, 3.5V6, 2.5TD, 2.8TD

Price from
£20,400

Manufactured in
Japan

Mitsubishi Space Gear

People carriers are inevitably large, but the Space Gear is about as large as they get this side of a small bus. The floor is completely flat from front footwell to the tail end, allowing passengers to move around easily. Seven or eight seats are available, with the rearmost flipping up to the sides when not required.

The Space Gear has an in-line front engine driving the rear wheels, with four-wheel-drive an option. This uses the system from the Shogun which, Mitsubishi claims, gives the Space Gear outstanding all-terrain performance. Top models get electronically controlled suspension. Popular in Europe and Japan, the Space Gear is not sold in the UK.

Best All-Rounder: Space Gear 2.8 TD

Body styles
MPV

Engine capacity
2.0, 2.4, 3.0V6, 2.5TD, 2.8TD

Price from
£n.a.

Manufactured in
Japan

Mitsubishi Montero/Challenger

The Challenger is a new hybrid from Mitsubishi, combining the chassis of the Shogun with the front of the L200 pickup and a new five-door estate body behind. By cutting down on the costly construction of the Shogun, a whole new sector of more budget conscious-buyers has been targeted.

Versatility is the other key to the Challenger's appeal. The dual floor contains a hidden cargo box. There's a storage cargo area with the seats folded and of course there's full-off-road ability with four-wheel drive. Engines are familiar from the Shogun - 3.0-litre V6 with 185bhp, 2.5-litre and 2.8-litre turbo-diesels producing 105 and 125bhp respectively.

Best All-Rounder: Challenger 2.5 TD

Body styles	Price from
Estate	£n.a.
Engine capacity	**Manufactured in**
3.0V6, 3.5V6, 2.8TD	Japan

Mitsubishi FTO

The stunning FTO is one of those cars that the Japanese keep to themselves. A thoroughly good looking coupe, it combines distinctive styling with some real technical interest, particularly in the top-of-the-range model.

This 2.0-litre V6 has variable valve timing which gives it a Jekyll and Hyde character. Below 6,000rpm it feels pretty ordinary, but take it through to 8,000rpm and 200bhp is unleashed. A five-speed gearbox is standard but the clever automatic has a 'sport' mode in which the gears are selected manually by flicking the lever back and forth, just like a Touring Car. Humbler FTOs are available with a 1.8 or lower-powered V6.

Best All-Rounder: FTO 2.0 GPX

Body styles
Coupe
Engine capacity
1.8, 2.0V6
Price from
£n.a.
Manufactured in
Japan

Mitsubishi Magna

Mitsubishi's contender in Australia's fiercely competitive family car market was the winner of the prestigious Wheels Magazine Car of the Year in 1996.

Manufactured in both saloon and estate versions, the entry-level Executive comes with a 2.4-litre four-cylinder engine with the option of a 3.0 V6. Upscale Advance or Altera versions get the V6, with the top-of-the-range Verada an ideal cruiser with its 3.5 V6. This particular version is also manufactured in left-hand-drive and exported to the US to be sold as the Diamante. The new 3.0 V6 Sports sedan gets a competent Tiptronic shifter, lowered suspension and body enhancements.

Best All-Rounder: Magna Advance 3.0 V6

Body styles
Saloon, Estate
Engine capacity
2.4, 3.0V6, 3.5V6
Price from
Aus $27,000
Manufactured in
Australia

morgan

Morgan

No other manufacturer causes enthusiasts to don the rose-tinted glasses more than Morgan. On paper, the archetypal British roadster built in the Malvern Hills simply doesn't make sense, but that is to miss the point entirely. With a solid streak of yesteryear running through it, a Morgan is simply one of those cars that you either love or hate. Ironically, the reasons for either stance are probably the same. The cars are from another era, compromised, lacking accepted creature comforts and very different from anything a modern driver will be used to. The family-owned factory only slowly changes its ways and that wins it both friends and enemies. The bar-room arguments will continue to run and run...

Plus 4

Morgan 4/4

Customers for a Morgan are unique, just like their cars. Whether the economy is in boom or bust, you can always be sure of one thing - there will be a waiting list for a Morgan. Patience comes as standard as delivery times are quoted in years rather than weeks.

Four models are on offer - the 4/4, Plus 4 (in two and four seater form) and storming Rover V8-powered Plus 8 - although in practice it's a case of picking your engine and then the sky's the limit, the car being built to your exact requirements. Engine choice ranges from a 1.8 right up to the 4.6-litre V8 from the Range Rover. Morgan has even embraced modern-day safety needs too as driver and passenger airbags are now available as options.

Best All-Rounder: Morgan Plus 8

Plus 8

Body styles Convertible
Engine capacity 1.8, 2.0, 4.0V8, 4.6V8
Price from £20,000
Manufactured in England

Nissan

Nissan's product line-up covers all the major areas apart from convertible sport cars, aiming for the same volume markets as Ford and Fiat in Europe and Asia, and the Big Three in the States. As a manufacturer the company often fails quite to hit the mark. While many of its cars are really very good indeed, notably the Micra, Almera and Primera, they lack the visual appeal that Ford, for example, does so well. If you can get past that, and the uniformly plain interiors, Nissans can be satisfying cars, though there is little hope for the Serena.

Nissan Primera

Like the smaller Almera, the Nissan Primera has got itself a reputation in the fiercely-contested business market not only for its excellent build quality and its prowess as a driver's car, but also for its unadventurous styling.

Not that that matters when you get behind the wheel however because, barring the diesel-engined models, any Primera from the entry-level 1.6 up to the flagship 148bhp 2.0-litre GT will put a smile on the driver's face when it is shown a challenging open road. It's the same inside where the interior is functional but bland and of a reasonable size, if not the largest in its class. Available as a four-door saloon and five-door hatchback, an estate version has recently joined the line-up too.

Best All-Rounder: Primera 2.0 SRi

Body styles Hatchback, Saloon, Estate
Engine capacity 1.6, 2.0, 2.0TD
Price from £13,800
Manufactured in UK, Japan

Nissan Micra

A recent face-lift and a fresh dashboard has given the Micra a well-deserved new lease of life. It was good enough to be the first Japanese car to win the European Car of the Year award and it remains a fundamentally sound machine. If the Micra's engines no longer seem the pinnacle of refinement, they still perform well and offer good fuel economy.

With or without power steering, the Micra is easy to drive. Parking is helped by the compact size, which in turn is the car's weakness. Newer superminis are a touch bigger, and can offer better accommodation for passengers and their luggage.

Best All-Rounder: Micra 1.0 GX

Body styles
Hatchback

Engine capacity
1.0, 1.3

Price from
£8,300

Manufactured in
UK

Nissan Almera

Nissan is fast earning itself a reputation for producing fine-handling cars with the Primera, the previous Sunny and now the Almera. Unfortunately, it's also getting a name for building some pretty dull-looking cars too and the Almera is no different.

Although there's a fine range of engines with 1.4 and 1.6-litre units and a 2.0-litre diesel all on offer, due to that fine handling it's the sportier versions that hog the limelight. There's the SRi warm-hatch and the flagship 141bhp 2.0-litre GTi. With a good level of reliability and plenty of interior space, those looks both inside and out fail to complete an otherwise impressive package.

Best All-Rounder: Almera 1.6 SRi

Body styles
Hatchback, Saloon

Engine capacity
1.4, 1.6, 2.0, 2.0D

Price from
£10,000

Manufactured in
Japan

Nissan QX

Like the Legend, Xedos 9 and Camry, the Nissan QX joins the long list of Japanese executive saloons that are all capable but lacking that vital factor for success in the company car park - envy. As with those rivals, the QX is a big seller in other worldwide markets (notably the USA), but European buyers have yet to catch on.

The big Nissan is offered with a choice of two smooth V6 engines, either 2.0 or 3.0-litre - the former coming in S, SE or SEL trims. The QX's on-road manners might not match the same high standards set by its refined engines, but there is a vast amount of equipment and interior space. Good value - but with heavy depreciation, it needs to be.

Best All-Rounder: QX 2.0 SE

Body styles
Saloon

Engine capacity
2.0V6, 3.0V6

Price from
£19,700

Manufactured in
Japan, US

Nissan 200SX

With nondescript styling on its launch, the Nissan 200SX failed to hit the headlines despite its promising front engined, rear-wheel-drive layout. With revised looks that's now changed (on the outside at least), but the 200SX still lacks the excitement and character provided by more recent competition such as the Fiat Coupe and Alfa Romeo GTV.

However, the Nissan can boast superb performance from its 197bhp 2.0-litre turbocharged engine, a high level of equipment (especially with the optional Touring pack), good value and a reasonable driving experience. The interior may be tight, particularly for those in the back, but the 200SX is entertaining all the same.

Best All-Rounder: 200SX

Body styles
Coupe

Engine capacity
2.0, 2.0 turbo

Price from
£21,800

Manufactured in
Japan

Nissan Serena

It may have arrived on the market a lot earlier than most of its competition and have the rare boast of offering eight seats, but the Nissan Serena cannot compete dynamically in the modern-day MPV class.

The Serena's engine sits under the floor as in a van, giving it not only tall and narrow looks, but a high-up feel on the road compromising handling as a result. Of the three engines - 1.6, 2.0 petrol and 2.3-litre diesel - only the 2.0-litre can offer anything like reasonable performance as the others are dismally slow. Aside from a bargain price tag and the 8-seater accommodation though, there's little else to recommend it.

Best All-Rounder: Serena 2.0

Body styles
MPV

Engine capacity
1.6, 2.0, 2.3D

Price from
£15,600

Manufactured in
Japan

Nissan Terrano II

With its sister car, the Ford Maverick, no longer on sale, Nissan's Terrano has effectively lost its closest competition. And the less rivals that Nissan's baby off-roader has, the better. With the arrival of the Freelander, Honda CR-V and Toyota RAV4, things are hotting up in the sub-£20,000 off-roader market and Nissan's dated entry is sure to continue to struggle.

Available in three and five-door forms, the Terrano's on-road manners will come as a pleasant surprise to those moving to it from a normal car. However, its car-like styling and mediocre off-road ability means it doesn't win friends among mud-plugging fans.

Best All-Rounder: Terrano 2.7TD

Body styles
Estate

Engine capacity
2.4, 2.7TD

Price from
£16,700

Manufactured in
Spain

Nissan Patrol

The new Nissan Patrol has not only lost the Tonka toy looks of its predecessor, but also some of its appeal. Make no mistake, the Patrol is still big even compared to most other 4x4s and its off-road ability is certainly not in doubt, but with those more-rounded lines has come a change in character.

That's mainly due to the lack of choice in the UK with only one engine available - a 2.8-litre turbo-diesel with 128bhp and dreadful performance - other world markets having the further option of a 4.5-litre petrol unit. Still, the Patrol has a fair amount of equipment and comes in three or five-door bodystyles, the latter with seven seats as standard.

Best All-Rounder: Patrol 5dr

Body styles
Estate

Engine capacity
4.5, 2.8TD, 4.2TD

Price from
£21,200

Manufactured in
Japan

Nissan Skyline

1999 sees the introduction of the all-new R34 Skyline range. As before there is a saloon and coupe on offer, with a choice of three six cylinder engines. Two are merely sporty - the 153bhp 2.0-litre and the 197bhp 2.5. The real excitement, however, comes from the 276bhp 2.5 turbo, which could form the basis of the new GTR.

It is this top sporting version that gets all the kudos, hardly surprising as it has the performance to severely frighten many a Porsche or Ferrari. A much stiffer body shell, new suspension plus four-wheel-drive and four-wheel-steering look likely to ensure that the Skyline GTR remains a daunting proposition.

Best All-Rounder: Skyline GT-R

Body styles
Saloon, Coupe

Engine capacity
2.0, 2.5, 2.5 turbo

Price from
£50,000

Manufactured in
Japan

Oldsmobile

General Motors' oldest division - it hit 100 last year - is currently at a crossroads. Some in GM's executive suites feel Oldsmobile has lost its identity and direction, and should be quietly shuttered. Others see the latest models - cars like the new Alero, the classy Intrigue and luxurious Aurora - attracting new buyers, buyers more likely to buy an import than another GM model. Oldsmobile's future is still far from certain, but with more well-designed, high-quality product in its model line-up, its chances of long-term survival seem more assured.

Oldsmobile Intrigue

Intrigued? Of course. That's why Oldsmobile's handsome new Omega-sized Intrigue is the official car of the X-Files cult TV show. It is also one of GM's most-appealing cars; attractively-shaped, a delight to drive, and very competitively-priced. It's also the first to feature GM's important new 3.5-litre 24-valve V6.

Bolt a Lexus badge on the Intrigue's boot lid and few would be the wiser - except when it came time to pay. At the equivalent of £14,000, this swoopy Olds is a bargain. New, optional 3.5 V6 is silky-smooth and refined, while even the standard pushrod 3.8-litre V6 offers refinement coupled with tugboat levels of torque.

Best All-Rounder: Intrigue GL 3.5

Body styles Saloon, Estate
Engine capacity 3.5V6, 3.8V6
Price from $20,800
Manufactured in US

Intrigue

Oldsmobile Alero   *new!*

Oldsmobile's role at General Motors is to try and stop GM owners migrating to Accords and Camrys. As an import fighter, the all-new '99 Olds Alero should do a fine job. Clean, handsome styling, punchy four-pot and V6 engines, and sporty handling should put the Alero high on people's shopping lists.

Take your pick from a sexy two-door coupe, or a four-door saloon that looks like a two-door coupe. Also chose between a gutsy 2.4-litre four-cylinder, or a smooth-revving 3.4-litre V6. Both are lively performers; although the four-cylinder makes more of a racket. The interiors are nicely-packaged and laid-out, especially the elegant coupe which boasts full four-seater accommodation.

Best All-Rounder: Alero saloon

Body styles Saloon, Coupe
Engine capacity 2.4, 3.4V6
Price from £16,200
Manufactured in US

Alero

Perodua Nippa

A small sub-supermini, Malaysia's Nippa may jog a few memories, for it last sold in the UK as the Japanese-built Daihatsu Mira and Cuore in the mid-1990s. Like many of these city cars originally designed for congested road conditions, it packs a surprising amount into its short length, including four passenger doors.

Power comes from a three-cylinder 850cc engine which can turn out a remarkable turn of speed if it is worked hard, which it seems to thrive on. It's very economical at the pumps too, and while no-one is going to pretend that the Nippa can compete with modern cars in terms of refinement or safety features, it's cheap and it's fun.

Best All-Rounder: Nippa EX

Body styles	Price from
Hatchback	£5,000

Engine capacity	Manufactured in
850	Malaysia

Plymouth Prowler

Cars just don't come much cooler than this. Get out your Ray-Bans, turn-up your collar, and cruise. Chrysler's funky hot-rod for the nineties goes into '99 with an all-new, all-alloy 3.5-litre V6 that cranks out a healthy 253bhp, plus the kind of bright yellow paint that will fricassee retinas at 50 paces.

OK, so the new 3.5-litre motor still isn't a V8, but at least the Prowler can now chirp its 20-inch rear tyres, and squirt to 60mph from zero in a creditable 6.5 seconds. There's still no place to stow any luggage, but who cares when you're driving a car as hip as this.

Best All-Rounder: Prowler with optional trailer

Body styles	Price from
Convertible	$40,000

Engine capacity	Manufactured in
3.5V6	US

peugeot

Peugeot

While superficially Peugeot could be viewed as just another manufacturer of family cars, there is much more to the brand than that. Peugeot has always managed to combine pleasing looks with a well-honed chassis - one that gives one of the most comfortable rides on the market yet has appeal for those who enjoy fast driving too. The new 206 supermini looks certain to follow that trend, dropping into a space in the range which will be vacated by deletion of the most expensive 106 models and cheaper versions of the 306. The other big news is a new 2.0-litre direct injection turbo-diesel. Diesels are an area where Peugeot excels, so expect good things.

206 XS

206 XT

Peugeot 206   *new!*

The sensuous lines of the new 206 are bound to re-awaken enthusiasm for the French marque, filling the void left after the 205 was finally canned. That car was especially good to drive, and there is little reason to think that the 206 will not take that a step further. Engines range from 1.1 to 1.6-litres initially, with a new 1.9-litre diesel. Power steering is standard on all.

Inside the 206 is as roomy as the best superminis, with a great deal of attention given to practical measures like stowage space. Going against the appeal are the hard, grainy plastics - too harsh to lend any warmth to the interior.

Best All-Rounder: Too early to tell

Body styles
Hatchback
Engine capacity
1.1, 1.4, 1.6, 1.9D
Price from
£8,500
Manufactured in
France

Peugeot 106

Peugeot's 106 may be one of the prettier superminis around but, along with its sister car the Citroen Saxo, its interior packaging has been overtaken by rivals such as the Fiat Punto and VW Polo - although that won't be so much of a problem when the larger 206 arrives.

Meanwhile, the 106 is offered with a wide range of engines. The entry-level 1.0 and 1.1 are rather slow making the 1.4 the much better option. The 1.5-litre diesel is extremely economical and refined, but the stars of the 106 range are undoubtedly the more sporting versions with the warm hatch XS, scorching GTi flagship and the stripped-out, no-frills Ralley. With those, driver enjoyment comes top of the list.

Best All-Rounder: 106 1.6 XS

Body styles	Price from
Hatchback	£8,000

Engine capacity	Manufactured in
1.0, 1.1, 1.4, 1.6, 1.5D	France, Spain

Peugeot 306

Although it's been around since 1993, the 306 still has some claims to the small/medium sector class leadership. In 1997 its svelte looks were enhanced and also an estate variant arrived.

The Peugeot enjoys popularity by doing most things well - petrol engines, interior, load-space and pricing and by some things excellently - turbo-diesel engines and driver appeal. The driving experience is best in class even now, offering an impeccable blend of ride and handling, regardless of whether it's a cooking estate or the hottest of hatches - the GTi-6.

Best All-Rounder: 306 XSi 5dr

Body styles	Price from
Hatchback, Saloon, Estate	£11,200

Engine capacity 1.4, 1.6, 1.8, 2.0, 1.9 D, 1.9TD	Manufactured in France, UK

Peugeot 406

The 406 was the first mainstream family car to approach Mondeo levels of competence when it was introduced in 1995. Since then some new engines have been installed and an estate has become available. In 1996, the Coupe - surely one of the classiest-looking at any price - was unveiled.

As a saloon or estate, the 406 combines the roominess and driving appeal of class leaders with a ride comfort and refinement that's better than any of them. The 1.8 and 2.0-litre petrol lack low and mid-range pulling power, but the turbocharged 2.0T addresses this problem. The 2.1-litre turbo-diesel version is, as usual for Peugeot, a great choice.

Best All-Rounder: 406 2.0 SRi Turbo

Body styles	Price from
Saloon, Estate	£14,100

Engine capacity	Manufactured in
1.6, 1.8, 2.0, 2.0 turbo, 3.0V6, 1.9TD, 2.1TD	France

Peugeot 605

Like Citroen, Peugeot has always struggled to succeed outside of France with its big executive saloons. At the outset, it was too similar to the smaller 405 to draw serious customers and now, with the arrival of the excellent 406, it's a wonder that Peugeot sells any at all.

Available with a 2.0-litre turbo petrol engine or a 2.1 turbo-diesel, the 605 may offer a luxurious interior and plenty of equipment for the money but it's dated and makes a less and less convincing argument for itself as time goes on. With depreciation to make your bank manager weep, if you want a comfortable Peugeot your money's better spent on a high-specification 406.

Best All-Rounder: 605 2.1 SRDT

Body styles
Saloon

Engine capacity
2.0, 2.0 turbo, 2.9V6, 2.1TD, 2.4TD

Price from
£23,300

Manufactured in
France

Peugeot 806

Peugeot's entry into the people-carrier market with the 806 has been largely met with apathy from the MPV-buying public compared to the big sellers from Ford and VW. But beyond the 806's awkward looks and those van-like sliding doors (which are a boon), it represents an impressive package.

Powered by a 2.0-litre petrol or a superb 1.9-litre turbo-diesel engine (a 2.0 petrol turbo is available in some markets), the 806 is not as roomy as the competition, but all models get twin airbags, air conditioning and remote central locking. The interior also boasts a dash-mounted gearlever allowing a step-through facility from front to back.

Best All-Rounder: 806 1.9TD

Body styles
MPV

Engine capacity
1.8, 2.0, 2.0 turbo, 1.9TD, 2.1TD

Price from
£17,70

Manufactured in
France

Pontiac

This is General Motors' so-called 'Excitement' division. Its buyers are younger, more style-conscious and want their cars to look red-hot. Subtlety takes a back seat to aggression here. Witness the latest Grand Am with its jet fighter rear wing, the Firebird Trans Am with its flared bonnet nostrils, and the Grand Prix, with its 'wide track', ready-to-pounce look.

Grand AM

Pontiac Grand Am

This is not a car for shy, retiring types. With its swoopy lines, dramatic, corrugated side panelling, and a rear wing that could have come off an F-15 jet fighter, the Mondeo-sized '99 Grand Am is about as subtle as a train crash. And Pontiac thinks that's just fine.

Sharing its platform with the new Oldsmobile Alero, the Grand Am pins its colours to the performance side. The standard 2.4-litre four-cylinder cranks out 150bhp, while the optional 3.4-litre V6 is good for 170bhp. For the moment, only a four-speed auto is on offer - the five-speed manual comes next year.

Best All-Rounder: Grand Am GT 4dr
Body styles Saloon **Engine capacity** 2.4, 3.4V6 **Price from** $15,900 **Manufactured in** United States

Grand Prix

Pontiac Grand Prix

Stance is everything with sports saloons. For the all-new Grand Prix, Pontiac has coined the phrase 'Wide Track' to highlight the car's dramatic stance. And, at over six feet wide, the Grand Prix does have that hunkered-down, ready-to-pounce look. It's also unusual in that both the two-door coupe and four-door saloon share almost identical profiles.

The Grand Prix goes as well as it looks. The top GTP model comes with 240bhp supercharged V6, while even the basic SE version uses a 3.1-litre 'six'. A rigid body structure helps provide chuckable handling, and despite all that power going through the front wheels, the steering is free from wayward tendencies and is decently accurate.

Best All-Rounder: Grand Prix GT 3.8
Body styles Saloon **Engine capacity** 3.1V6, 3.1V6 Supercharged **Price from** $18,800 **Manufactured in** US

Pontiac Firebird

Fact: You can't get a better bang for the buck than a Firebird. For the price of a dull-as-dishwater, family saloon, the Firebird Formula packs a Tyson-like, 305bhp punch from its fire-breathing 5.7-litre V8. With more wings than the Red Arrows, this potent Pontiac grabs attention wherever it goes.

Don't expect too much sophistication here. The Firebird is a heavyweight champ that delivers it V8 muscle in an explosion of raw, rumbling roaring power. Standstill to 60mph comes up in under 5.5 seconds, and with its long-legged six-speed 'box slotted in top, it'll run to 170-plus mph.

Best: Firebird Formula
Body styles Coupe
Engine capacity
3.8V6, 5.7V8
Price from $18,200
Manufactured in United States

Porsche

After years when all Porsche seemed to do was offer yet another development of the 911 (as well as repeatedly winning at Le Mans), the recent flurry of activity comes as something of a shock. First the Boxster, then the new 911, both designed to entice new buyers into the fold as well as keeping the regular customers happy. The first objective seems assured, for the Boxster is relatively affordable and currently in high demand - Porsche has opened a second production line in Finland to cope. All objective tests show the new 911 to be a better one than the outgoing model, though the die-hards mourn the smoothing out of the old car's rough edges.

Boxster

Porsche Boxster

Porsche's 'budget' Boxster has taken off in the biggest possible way, and for sound reasons. First, it is cheap - for a Porsche. Second, it still feels like a Porsche - solid, well-built, touches carried over from the 911 and the distinctive six-cylinder growl. This time the engine is mid-mounted, so there is useful luggage space front and rear.

Significantly this is a Porsche that is easy to drive, both in town and at high speed. With 2.5 litres the performance is strong without being breathtaking, but importantly, it is a thoroughly rewarding car as well as being as practical as any sports car can be.
Best All-Rounder: Boxster

Body styles Convertible **Engine capacity** 2.5 **Price from** £34,000 **Manufactured in** Germany, Finland

911 convertible

Porsche 911

It may still be called a 911, and still look like the original, but this one is genuinely new from the ground up. Opening the door and sliding inside the cockpit shows this is something different. There is more space, a dashboard that makes perfect sense, better pedals and an improved driving position.

The new water-cooled engine bursts energetically into life, though the sound is softer. The latest 911 still surges from the line like no other sports car, tearing to 60mph in 4.9 seconds. Rightly the 911 has progressed. Some buyers of the earlier cars might not appreciate it, but this is the most complete all-rounder Porsche has ever turned out.
Best All-Rounder: 911 Coupe

Body styles Coupe, Convertible **Engine capacity** 3.4
Price from £65,00
Manufactured in
Germany

911 coupe

proton

Proton

Proton started out as a car manufacturer by building superseded Mitsubishis. In the UK it was a huge success, offering great value for money and a long warranty to buyers who did not worry about having the latest design. Today's Protons still owe their heritage to Mitsubishi, something that is immediately obvious in the Compact, less so in the bigger model, the Persona, and its stylish coupe derivative. All are much better than those earlier cars, but they are also more expensive. The result is that Proton is now head-to-head with several other manufacturers - Daewoo and Hyundai for example - that offer a similar or more tempting deal, making business all the tougher.

Compact

Proton Compact

Sharing the same Proton family look as the larger Persona, the Compact is basically a previous generation Mitsubishi Colt. Available in three-door hatchback form, the Compact is certainly one of the largest superminis around in terms of sheer dimensions, but interior space is actually smaller than most.

Like the larger Persona, the Compact offers a quality interior and good looks combined with a choice of three engines - 1.3, 1.5 or 1.6-litres. However, the Compact's on road manners are poor and it lacks refinement. The comprehensive warranty package may be all in the Compact's favour, but even there Proton is fast being caught and matched by its rivals.

Best All-Rounder: Compact 1.5 GLSi

Body styles Hatchback **Engine capacity** 1.3, 1.5, 1.6 **Price from** £7,800 **Manufactured in** Malaysia

Persona Saloon

Proton Persona

The budget market has become even more competitive in recent years with the likes of Hyundai and Skoda improving their standards and the arrival of yet another player, Daewoo. But Malaysian firm Proton continues to offer an appealing package for those after peace of mind from a lengthy warranty.

Persona Coupe

The Persona comes as a four-door saloon, five-door hatchback and now a sportier two-door coupe. Engine choice ranges from a lowly 1.3-litre up to a 114bhp 1.8 and there is also a 2.0-litre turbodiesel, although the latter's performance leaves something to be desired. The coupe, meanwhile, gets its own uprated 1.8-litre engine with 133bhp. The Persona is effortless and easy to drive although lacks the image and quality feel of its competition.

Best All-Rounder: Persona 1.8EXi

Body styles Hatchback, Saloon, coupe
Engine capacity 1.5, 1.6, 1.8. 2.0TD
Price from £9,200
Manufactured in Malaysia

Renault

Renault has been through a very busy period over the past couple of years, producing a host of new or revised models. The Espace, Megane Scenic and Clio are all new, while the Laguna and Twingo are both revised. Such dynamism ensures that the French manufacturer stays up there with the big players in Europe. Not surprisingly 1999 will be a year of fewer changes. Further engines will be added to the Clio, including a 1.6-litre 110 bhp sports version and a 2.0-litre hot hatch. Renault's new 24-valve V6 engine will find its way into the Espace, and later in the year, the Megane will get a new nose in a facelift. Nothing radical then, but at the moment Renault is flying high.

Renault Clio   *new!*

The family likeness is still evident in the new, cheekier Clio, even though it's essentially an all-new car. What has been carried over are the engines - 1.2, 1.4, and 1.6-litre petrol units and a 1.9-litre diesel - with a hot new 100 bhp 16-valve version following soon.

The much improved refinement is now up there with the best of the superminis, and while the steering and handling doesn't reach the same standards, they're not at all bad. The interior lacks some of the class and space of its rivals but it is well equipped for the price, so it looks like the Clio's continued popularity is guaranteed.

Best All-Rounder: Clio 1.2 RT

Body styles Hatchback
Engine capacity 1.2, 1.4, 1.6, 2.0, 1.9D
Price from £8,400
Manufactured in France, Spain

Renault Megane

With the Scenic having been such a huge success for Renault both in the UK and abroad, the rest of the Megane range and its wide selection of bodystyles has been undeservedly pushed into the shade.

The Megane comes as a five-door hatchback, four-door saloon (with a huge boot), two-door coupe (cramped rear seats), convertible or even an estate (which doesn't come to the UK). The drop-top incidentally, can be had with a clever optional road box that turns it from a four-seater to a two-seater with an extended boot. Dynamically though, the Megane is being left behind by younger competition, it rides well but, barring the diesels, the engines hardly represent the cutting edge of refinement and there's not much driver involvement.

Best All-Rounder: Megane 1.9TDi RT

Body styles	Price from
Hatchback, Saloon	£11,700
Engine capacity	**Manufactured in**
1.4, 1.6, 2.0, 1.9TD	France, Spain

Renault Laguna

A distinctive appearance can sharply divide opinion, but the Laguna's elegant lines seem to have met universal approval. Five years after its launch in 1993, a minor facelift has done little but tweak a few details to freshen the look. Mechanically there is an impressively powerful new 1.6-litre engine.

The Laguna's interior is pleasing to the eye and spacious too, though if the hatchback doesn't quite offer enough space, then the estate should. Competitive pricing, a fine ride, reasonable (but not class leading) handling and good refinement and performance keep the Laguna in the lead pack. Faults? Few real ones, though reliability hasn't been perfect.

Best All-Rounder: Laguna 2.0-16v RTi

Body styles
Hatchback, Estate

Engine capacity
1.6, 2.0, 3.0V6, 2.2D, 2.2TD

Price from
£13,600

Manufactured in
France. Spain

Renault Safrane

For numerous reasons, Renault's big executive cars, like their Citroen and Peugeot rivals, have never had much sales success outside of France. A hatchback bodystyle on a big executive car has never caught on in the UK and the re-design with a Ferrari-style egg-crate front grille has only marginally improved sales.

At the same time, the range has been slimmed down to just two engine choices - a 2.0-litre 16-valve as seen in the Laguna and a 20-valve five-cylinder 2.5 from the Volvo S70. Dynamically, the Safrane performs well with an excellent ride, comfortable seats and lots of room, but there's little driver involvement and the handling feels soggy - a shame given the performance of the 2.5.

Best All-Rounder: Safrane 2.5 Executive

Body styles
Hatchback

Engine capacity
2.2, 2.5

Price from
£19,300

Manufactured in
France

Renault Sport Spider

The breathtaking Sport Spider just shows what a major manufacturer can do when freed from normal constraints. The startling styling, aluminium chassis and race-car feel combine to make this one of the most extraordinary cars you can buy for the road.

On paper the Spider is not as fast as an Elise, but it sure feels it. The levels of grip are enormous, and although the steering weights up as cornering speeds increase, the Spider always feels reassuringly stable. But with no roof, side windows or door locks it is a totally impractical car to live with. Who cares!

Best All-Rounder: Sport Spider 2.0

Body styles
Convertible

Engine capacity
2.0

Price from
£26,600

Manufactured in
France

Renault Twingo

Renault has given the Twingo a mid-life facelift to help cope with increased competition from the likes of the Ka, Seicento and Arosa. Cosmetically the changes are minimal with new equipment levels and trims and mildly restyled front lights, but underneath there's a stronger bodyshell for improved crash performance.

The only engine choice is the smooth 1.2-litre DIET engine as seen in the Clio and the Twingo will get a BMW M3-style sequential manual system early in 1999. But despite its good ride, reasonable interior space and the latest changes, UK motorists will still have to wait until at least 2002 for the next generation Twingo.

Best All-Rounder: Twingo 1.2

Body styles
Hatchback

Engine capacity
1.2

Price from
£6,000

Manufactured in
France, Spain, Colombia

Megane Scenic

Such is the soundness of the Scenic concept that not only has it becomes Renault's best-selling Megane, but every other manufacturer will shortly be aping the idea. It is an impressive combination of flexibility and interior space, all for just £1,000 more than the Megane hatchback.

The Scenic sits five adults comfortably with plenty of leg and foot room. The three back seats are independently mounted and can be moved back and forth or removed individually. There are storage spaces everywhere, including under the floor. The Scenic is certainly not a car for the enthusiastic driver, but its character and versatility quickly become compulsive.

Best All-Rounder: Scenic 1.9TDi RT

Body styles
MPV

Engine capacity
1.4, 1.6, 2.0, 1.9TD

Price from
£13,000

Manufactured in
France, Spain

Renault Espace

Renault is trying to market the latest Espace as the Range Rover of the people-carrier world and has gone the same route as Chrysler's Voyager in offering a standard model and a longer Grand Espace for extra luggage space.

Three engines are available from a 2.0-litre (now in manual and automatic forms) and a thirsty 3.0-litre V6 to a very refined 2.2, 115bhp turbo-diesel. A space-age interior with plenty of useful pockets shows Renault's excellent forethought of design; the floor-rails that run the entire length of the car in the flagship RXE allow almost infinite seating combinations. You pay a premium compared to rivals, but it's worth it.

Best All-Rounder: Espace 2.2td RT

Body styles
MPV

Engine capacity
2.0, 3.0V6, 2.2TD

Price from
£19,700

Manufactured in
France

Rolls-Royce

The near farce that was the Rolls-Royce sale in 1998 has apparently been settled. Volkswagen bought the firm from owner Vickers, although VW loses the right to the Rolls-Royce name in a few years to BMW. Today, with a new model in its armoury Rolls-Royce looks in a better shape than for a long time. The V12-powered Silver Seraph offers a genuine advance over the superseded saloons, and even though some mourned the loss of sovereignty when BMW became so involved in the development of the new model, that no longer seems to matter.

Rolls-Royce Silver Seraph

new!

With the Silver Seraph Rolls-Royce has produced its first totally new saloon in years, so it's ironic that it could be about to suffer a few hiccups with the recent takeover by Volkswagen. Despite on-paper agreements for BMW to continue supply numerous parts for the Seraph (not least its engine and drivetrain), it's hard to see exactly how the long-term situation will be resolved.

For the time being though, the Seraph gets a 5.4-litre V12 engine with a not-inconsiderable 322bhp. Inside, there's the usual Rolls-Royce luxury touches with unmatched levels of wood and leather all lovingly hand crafted. And, with new elegant exterior lines, it will be a shame if the takeover problems hamper the Seraph becoming one of the most successful cars ever to come from Crewe.

Best All-Rounder: Silver Seraph

Body styles
Saloon
Engine capacity
5.4V12
Price from
£155,000

Manufactured in
England

ROVER

Rover

It was always going to take time for the full influence of BMW's ownership of Rover to become obvious, but the autumn of 1998 saw the first major new BMW-influenced car, the Rover 75. Sadly Rover would not release details until after we published, but the new car will replace both the 600 and 800 ranges when it goes on sale in the spring. 1999 also sees changes to the 400 range as well as the MGF, and an all-new Mini is due in 2000. On the four-wheel-drive front the Freelander has been enormously successful for Rover. A revised Discovery builds on this, offering more room and more power, including a five-cylinder turbo-diesel.

Rover MGF

In a market increasingly brimming with new sports cars, the MGF can hold its own with any of them. It is unique amongst its competitors in having a mid-engined layout for optimum balance and roadholding. This configuration, combined with the hydragas suspension, makes for perhaps the best ride/handling combination of any of the new generation of sportsters.

Both versions of the 1.8-litre K-series engines provide decent performance, but it's the VVC (Variable Valve Control) version that gives the real thrills. The only mild let-down is an interior which lacks the spark of imagination of some rivals and which places tall drivers a little too high up.

Best All-Rounder: MGF 1.8i

Body styles Convertible
Engine capacity 1.8, 1.8VVC
Price from £18,000
Manufactured in England

Rover 400

Rover has stuck to its guns with its size-strategy of the 400 and smaller 200 and it appears to have paid off. Sitting uncomfortably between the Escort and Mondeo, the 400 is available as a saloon or hatchback, the latter most belying the car's Japanese underpinnings (the 400 is a twin to the Honda Civic).

The engine range is considerable from 1.4 up to 2.0-litre petrols and including two very economical turbodiesels. The more powerful of the oil-burners also finds a home in the larger 600 and while lacking some refinement, has a good turn of performance. Although tight on interior space compared to some rivals, the classy feel of the Rover's cabin has meant that the 400, especially in saloon form with its added snob value, has proved popular.

Best All-Rounder: 416 5dr

Body styles	Price from
Hatchback, Saloon,	£13,500
Engine capacity	**Manufactured in**
1.4, 1.6, 1.8, 2.0, 2.5V6, 2.0TD	England

Rover 200

The 200 was the first Rover for a long time to be developed without Honda's help. Smaller than most of the Escort-class of family cars, it competes with them on price, a situation Rover justifies with the impressive trim and refinement. Excellent K-Series engines or a good turbo-diesel provide the power.

The 200 brims with showroom appeal. Pretty from the outside, there is a well designed and finished cabin that does Rover proud. The driving experience does too, with a composed ride which is the match of some cars in the class above. If it had more space inside, the 200 could steal class honours.

Best All-Rounder: 216 Si

Body styles
Hatchback

Engine capacity
1.1, 1.4, 1.6, 1.8, 2.0TD

Price from
£9,700

Manufactured in
England

Rover Mini

There isn't a lot that the Mini hasn't done. As if being a design template for forty years or more wasn't enough, it has dominated the world rally scene, robbed the Italians and become the first love of generations of car enthusiasts. Reality being what it is, though, it all has to end in 2000.

But for the meantime, the Sooper-Dooper-Cooper continues alongside the 1.3i: both demand a lot of money for privilege of ownership. Is it worth it? Sit awkwardly in the driver's seat and drive. If the hard ride doesn't kill you, laughter at the first corner will. Talk about going out on a high - the Mini is still an absolute hoot to drive.

Best All-Rounder: Mini Cooper

Body styles
Saloon

Engine capacity
1.3

Price from
£9,200

Manufactured in
England

Rover Niche

Based on the previous generation Rover models, the Tourer, Coupe and Cabriolet look positively jurassic compared to the newer models in the Rover showroom. The trio all get Rover's 1.6-litre K-Series engine, while the Coupe also has the 1.8-litre VVC unit from the the more powerful MGF.

All three models have the elegant and modern interior from the present 200, but it's precious little substitute. In its favour, the Coupe also gets removable glass roof panels to give it a T-bar roof, while SE versions of the Cabriolet have an electric roof. Interior space in both is tight, especially in the rear, while the Tourer is more of a lifestyle shooting-brake rather than a workhorse estate.

Best All-Rounder: Tourer 1.6

Body styles
Estate, Coupe, Convertible

Engine capacity
1.6, 1.8

Price from
£15,300

Manufactured in
England

Rover 600

The Rover 600's classy exterior design coupled to an interior full of wood, chrome and stainless steel has won it many fans. Certainly it offers a different approach to that of the Audi A4 and BMW 3-Series, with an accent more on luxury.

There's plenty of room for those in the front - the seats are particularly large - to back up that impression, though space in the back is not generous, and the ride is rather too firm. There is a wide range of engines, all of which perform well, though this is no sports saloon. The 600 is replaced by the Rover 75 in the Spring.

Best All-Rounder: 618 Si

Body styles
Saloon

Engine capacity
1.8, 2.0, 2.0 turbo, 2.3, 2.0TD

Price from
£15,700

Manufactured in
England

Rover 800

The 800 has the feel of a car kept in production for too long. The old Rover has simply been left behind in its build quality, ride comfort, refinement and handling. Inside, the narrowness of the cabin hurts its accommodation and rear headroom is tight.

On the move, the suspension smoothness is not up to today's levels for an executive car. Performance is fair, and positively impressive from the 2.5 V6 and turbo-charged Vitesse, both of which offer good refinement. But that, and the generous helping of wood and stainless steel, is not enough to save the range from mediocrity. Its replacement arrives in the Spring.

Best All-Rounder: 820T Vitesse

Body styles
Hatchback, Saloon, Coupe

Engine capacity
2.0, 2.0 turbo, 2.5V6, 2.5TD

Price from
£19,700

Manufactured in
England

ssang yong

Ssangyong

Ssangyong is one of those gigantic industrial conglomerates that blossom in the Far East, dealing in shipbuilding, construction and everything in-between. The car building side of the business is relatively young, but despite the help of British designers and the use of Mercedes-Benz engines and transmissions, things have not worked out. So it came as little surprise when, in mid-1998, the vehicle side of the business was swallowed up by Daewoo. In the short term the off-roaders will be badged as Daewoos, though it is far from clear what will happen to the Ssangyong Chairman, a mildly re-bodied version of the Mercedes-Benz E-Class.

Musso

Ssangyong Musso

The Musso's styling is a not altogether successful mixture of car and off-roader, but what is does offer is offers full four-wheel-drive ability for the price of a family estate. The engines are Mercedes-Benz-designed units. The turbo-diesel is refined, quiet but slow. The petrol 2.3 is a great all-rounder while the 3.2 accelerates like a scalded cat.

In terms of practicality the Musso beats most, with masses of room for passengers and a gigantic boot. Comfort levels are good, it rides well and steers with precision, but this bias towards road use means that off-road it falls behind the best.

Best All-Rounder: Musso 2.9TD GLS

Body styles Estate **Engine capacity** 2.3, 3.2, 2.8TD **Price from** £19,200 **Manufactured in** Korea

Ssangyong Korando

Korando

In the UK, the proposed transition to Daewoo has hindered Korando sales significantly, which is a shame. The well constructed, medium sized off-roader shows good engineering through and through, including two smooth, powerful engines from Mercedes-Benz.

Some of the cabin's ambience seems to have been inherited from the German marque too; there's an air of solidity throughout the interior spoiled only by the lack of 5-doors. And, although it copes well on and off-road, it remains to be seen whether as a Daewoo the Korando can do it in the golf club car park.

Best All-Rounder: Korando 2.3 GLS

Body styles Estate
Engines 2.3, 2.8D
Price from £16,000
Manufactured in Korea

S981 JYY

Saab

Like Vauxhall and Opel, Saab is owned by American giant General Motors. GM has, it seems, tried to ensure that new Saabs retain their individuality, though it got off to the rocky start with the last 900. That car, however, was transformed into the 9-3 in 1998 and now offers much more of what traditional Saab buyers appear to like. Within a year all 9-3s will be turbocharged, but in the short term they get more and more power - 185bhp, 200bhp and eventually a 225bhp 2.3-litre turbo. The impressive 9-5 also receives its long awaited 3.0 V6 Turbo as well as a range of estate models.

9-3 convertible

Saab 9-3

Saab says that there are over 1,000 changes in the transformation of the 900 into the 9-3, but fundamentally it is the same car. Modifications include a 9-5 grille, new seats and much development work on the chassis.

With both of the turbo-charged petrol engines the 9-3 can be a pleasure to drive, while the new "sporting" turbo-diesel is a delight. But even in its most powerful current form the 9-3 lacks the hard sporting edge of the BMW 3-Series. Instead it offers more practicality, space and a high degree of comfort for four large adults combined with a massive luggage capacity.

Best All-Rounder: 9-3 2.3SE

Body styles Saloon, Coupe;
Engine capacity 2.0, 2.3, 2.0 Turbo, 2.2TD
Price from £16,500
Manufactured in Sweden, Finland

9-3

Saab 9-5

Conservative in appearance, the 9-5 will win few beauty contests but will quickly win over those who drive it. Every engine is turbo-charged, and even the 2.0-litre provides responsive performance in town and on the motorway. The steering and handling are biased towards comfort, but are none the worse for that.

The interior of the higher specification models, all ruched leather and two-tone trim, has the ambience of a Jaguar, no mean feat in a car at this price. The 9-5 is spacious both for rear occupants and for luggage. The minor weaknesses are confined to the ride which is firm and the engine note of the four-cylinder cars.

Best All-Rounder: 9-5 2.3t SE

Body styles	Price from
Saloon, Estate	£22,000

Engine capacity	Manufactured in
2.0 turbo, 2.3 turbo, 3.0V6 turbo	Sweden

Saturn

Saturn EV1

It's the future, and you can drive it now. Available for lease in some of America's sunshine states - like California and Arizona - General Motors' EV1 is the world's first production electric vehicle. This slippery-shaped two-seater uses a pack of 26 batteries to power its 137bhp motor.

Range - or the lack of it - is the issue here. While GM claims 70 to 90 miles between charges, most owners are getting half that. But it's fun while it lasts. From standstill, it'll sprint to 60mph in a sports car-like 7.9 seconds, and handle itself with remarkable agility.

Best All-Rounder: EV1 with a full charge

Body styles	Price from
Coupe	$38,000

Engine capacity	Manufactured in
n/a	US

seat

Seat

Seat was passed around a bit in its early days, with both the Spanish Government and Fiat owning major stakes before its eventual sale to Volkswagen. There are still examples of the old cars around - basically 1980s Fiats without the build quality - but things have leapt ahead in the past five years. Now Seat's role in the VW Group is to build cars with a bit of brio, cars that will appeal to the young at heart, while beneath the skin having the qualities you get from a Volkswagen. With the only remaining suspect car in the range - the Toledo - replaced for 1999, the brief has been fulfilled.

Seat Toledo   *new!*

Chalk and cheese comes to mind when comparing the 1999 Toledo with the old model. The new car looks so right, with swooping sports saloon curves that contain real Latin flair, and are a million miles away from the dullard style of the outgoing Toledo.

Though technically it is a new Seat, the Toledo is not really an all-new car. Under the skin there is the much used mechanical package from the VW Golf which also forms the basis of the Skoda Octavia and Audi A3. That means some fine petrol and diesel engines, ranging from a lively 1.6 to a 180bhp 1.8 turbo.

Best All-Rounder: Too early to tell

Body styles Hatchback
Engine capacity 1.6, 1.8, 1.8 turbo, 1.9TD
Price from £12,500 (est)
Manufactured in Spain

Seat Arosa

As will always be the case with Seats of the future, the Arosa owes its parentage to Volkswagen. This time, though, Seat had the jump on VW's small car by well over a year, and the Arosa has already established itself to be an admirable little vehicle. Its three-door body houses 1.0 and 1.4-litre petrol engines and an incredibly frugal 1.7-litre diesel.

The Arosa feels a lot bigger inside than out, helped by the dashboard and switchgear straight out of the Ibiza. There's not a lot of room in the back or in the boot, but there is in the front and the refinement is as good as most superminis.

Best All-Rounder: Arosa 1.0

Body styles
Hatchback

Engine capacity
1.0, 1.4, 1.7D

Price from
£7,000

Manufactured in
Germany

Seat Ibiza/Cordoba

The efforts owner Volkswagen has put into the Spanish car-maker has improved both the quality and the design of its cars, yet they manage to retain some Spanish flair. Both the Ibiza supermini and its close cousins, the Cordoba saloon, coupe and estate, owe a strong allegiance to the VW Polo. 1999 sees a major facelift and a wider range including a 20-valve Turbo.

All have a solid feel and spacious interior. On the road, both the Ibiza and Cordoba are thoroughly capable cars. They feel tightly screwed together and are pleasant inside, but a slightly harsh ride spoils the comfort to some extent.

Best All-Rounder: Ibiza 1.4

Body styles
Hatchback, Saloon, Estate, Coupe

Engine capacity
1.4, 1.6, 1.8, 2.0, 1.9D, 1.9TD

Price from
£9,000

Manufactured in
Spain

Seat Alhambra

The Alhambra is the final piece in the VW Sharan/Ford Galaxy jigsaw. In truth it is the same as the other two vehicles, but with an accent on fun, hence the jazzy seats. As the least well known of the brands, the Alhambra compensates with better equipment levels. It is all standard 7-seater fare, but good non-the-less.

On the road the Alhambra offers a car-like driving position, while the stiff suspension prevents too much body roll. The 2.0-litre petrol engine is a refined and quiet cruiser, but not very lively. The turbodiesels are more desirable, especially the 110bhp TDi, while the 1.8 petrol turbo adds some welcome performance.

Best All-Rounder: Alhambra TDi 110

Body styles
MPV

Engine capacity
1.8, 1.8 turbo, 2.0, 1.9TD

Price from
£18,200

Manufactured in
Portugal

Skoda

In a way Volkswagen must have had a tougher job turning around Skoda than it did Seat. In the UK the Czech manufacturer was the subject to a level of ridicule that had forced Lancia out of the country for good. Yet in a few short years the cars and the image have been transformed, and now no respectable critic says anything but good things about the company. What has happened is that while the cars remain very competitively priced, the quality and the driving pleasure has improved immeasurably. The time was right for a bigger car, and it is here - the Octavia.

Skoda Felicia

The Felicia has won more budget car awards than anything else since it was launched in 1994 and it has just had a mild makeover which conforms to the Skoda corporate look. Both hatchback and estate versions offer great value by providing loads of space for supermini money. Today's cars feel well built and all give reasonable refinement. Ride and handling are some way off the best cars of its size, but as budget workhorses go, the Felicia is probably the best in the business.

Best All-Rounder: Felicia 1.6 GLXi

Body styles Hatchback, Estate, Pick-up
Engine capacity 1.1, 1.3, 1.6, 1.9D
Price from £7,000
Manufactured in Czech Republic

Skoda Octavia

With the Octavia, Skoda has moved into the larger car arena with instant success. This full-sized family car has the quality and ability of a Volkswagen, as it should - VW owns the company. Mechanically it has much in common with the new VW Golf, with the same petrol and turbodiesel engines.

That means it is a thoroughly pleasing car to drive - the 100bhp 1.6 is particularly well-suited (there is a slower 75bhp 1.6 too). Being a something of hybrid means that though there is plenty of width inside the car although rear legroom is more constrained than a Mondeo. But the massive boot makes up for this.

Best All-Rounder: Octavia 1.6 GLXi

Body styles	Price from
Hatchback, Estate	£11,500

Engine capacity	Manufactured in
1.6, 1.8, 1.9TD	Czech Republic

Shelby Series 1

Spiritual successor to the legendary AC Cobra, the Shelby Series 1 combines raw power with some space age technology. Take the curvy body of this 170mph two-seater. Made of carbon fibre, the bodyshell tips the scales at just 100lbs. Bolt-in a 325bhp Oldsmobile V8 and you get tyre-frying standstill-to-60mph sprinting in just over four seconds.

It may not be the prettiest sports car in the world, but when the Series 1 goes into full production later this year, it's likely to be one of the most-exciting. In addition to 325 horses, the Shelby has race-car suspension, and brakes the size of pizza dishes. Production will be limited to just 500 cars.

Best All-Rounder: Shelby Series 1

Body styles	Price from
Convertible	$97,500 (est)

Engine capacity	Manufactured in
4.0V8	US

subaru

Subaru

Subaru concentrates on four-wheel-drive. Not hulking great off-roaders, but ostensibly ordinary-looking family cars capable of getting where no ordinary family car can go when the going gets tough. It is a tactic that has worked well, for the cars are reasonably priced compared with the rather esoteric four-wheel-drive models offered by the mainstream manufacturers. Subaru's big car is the Legacy, which late in 1998 is replaced with an all-new model. Or at least the 2.5-litre estate car is, for the saloon and less-powerful estates continue well into 1999. Also coming soon is a turbocharged version of the Forester, plus more powerful 2.0-litre engines for that car and the Impreza.

Subaru Impreza

The Impreza is for drivers looking for something different to the run-of-the-mill small family car. Both the saloon and hatchback-cum-estate are equipped with four-wheel-drive, with a choice of flat-four engines, 2.0 and 2.0 Turbo. The 2.0 Sport model combines the Turbo's looks with the less powerful engine.

The Impreza comes across as a thoroughly likeable car to drive, handling extremely well, as it needs to with over 200bhp from the Turbo. This version offers performance more akin to a rally car, but even the standard 2.0-litre has a sporty burble to its nature. Interior space and comfort are about average for the Escort class.

Best All-Rounder: Impreza 2.0 Sport

Body styles
Saloon, Estate
Engine capacity
1.6, 2.0, 2.0 turbo, 2.5 turbo
Price from
£14,500
Manufactured in
Japan

Subaru Legacy

new!

1999 sees an all-new Legacy, but you will be hard pushed to spot the difference. Initially it will be sold as just the 2.5-litre estate, with saloons and smaller capacity estate models arriving throughout the year. As always, the Legacy's major selling point is its four wheel-drive which gives it a versatility matched by few other family cars.

Comfort levels of the current model are very good, with well-bucketed front seats providing excellent support, and generous legroom in the back. The Legacy is good to drive too, with good handling, a pliant ride and a strong and refined range of flat-four engines. It is to be hoped that the interior of the new car will also be a bit brighter.

Best All-Rounder: Legacy 2.5 Estate

Body styles
Saloon, Estate

Engine capacity
2.0, 2.0 turbo, 2.2, 2.5

Price from
£15,900

Manufactured in
Japan

Subaru Forester

The sensible, estate-like styling of the Forester is based around a permanent four-wheel-drive platform from the Impreza. Power comes from some obligatory four-cylinder boxer engines, with anything from a reasonable 120 to a mammoth 250bhp.

Even the base 2.0-litre engine powers the car well enough, the driving experience, aided by great ergonomics, is refined and relaxed. Impreza underpinnings give class leading handling and roadholding, whilst interior space is good all round - the large boot complemented by ample oddments space. It all helps make the Forester one of the better, if not the trendiest, sports utilities.

Best All-Rounder: Forester 2.0 Turbo

Body styles
Estate

Engine capacity
2.0, 2.0 turbo, 2.5

Price from
£16,500

Manufactured in
Japan

Subaru Justy

The latest Justy is one of the cheapest 4x4s on the market. Part of that cost benefit is due to its construction - it is a clone of the Suzuki Swift, built in Hungary and fitted with four-wheel-drive.

The four-wheel-drive system has the obvious benefits, though for less than enthusiastic drivers the extra traction will probably never be noticed until trying to accelerate up a steep, wet slope or drive on snow. Slack steering, a reluctant gearchange and a bouncy ride take the edge off the driving enjoyment. Inside, the cabin isn't as smart as a Ford Fiesta but rear seat legroom in the longer 5-door is generous.

Best All-Rounder: Justy 1.3 GX

Body styles
Hatchback

Engine capacity
1.3

Price from
£9,500

Manufactured in
Japan

Suzuki

After what seems like years of not very much happening at Suzuki cars, suddenly there has been a flurry of activity. Its two core off-roaders, the type of vehicle with which the bike maker made its name as a car manufacturer, have both been replaced. The crude old SJ is superseded by the altogether more promising Jimny, and the Vitara by the decidedly more up-market Grand Vitara. In 1999 there will be a new sub-supermini to replace the Alto, a joint venture with General Motors, built in Poland and Hungary. The lack-lustre Baleno gets a major facelift and gains a diesel engine - from Peugeot - for the first time.

Suzuki Alto

The anonymous Alto is a basic city car. It has an unremarkable 1.0-litre engine, three or five-doors and reasonable interior space for the class. The cost has been kept down by minimising options and by building the car in India. Thankfully it feels well screwed together so the package isn't too unrefined on the road.

Alto

Jimny   *new!*

The Jimny is Suzuki's replacement for the SJ, its budget off-roader that ran for almost two decades. One glance at the new model shows that this is a more upmarket offering. Where those early cars were really commercial vehicles which found a use as passenger cars, the 1999 Jimny is a much classier act.

Mechanically it relies on the traditional ladder-frame chassis, 1.3-litre engine and selectable two or four-wheel-drive. New suspension should improve the comfort and the handling, one of the major weak points of the old car. As before, the smallest Suzuki 4x4 will be cheap enough to have little in the way of direct competition.

Body styles Alto: Hatchback; Jimny: Estate
Engine capacity Alto: 0.7, 1.0; Jimny: 1.3
Price from Alto: £6,300; Jimny: £10,000 (est)
Manufactured in Alto: India; Jimny: Japan

Jimny

Suzuki Wagon R+

The hideous Wagon R+ has been the best selling car in Japan, where city cars are in their element regardless of looks. Fitted with a 1.0 or new 1.2-litre four-cylinder engine, the Wagon promises economical town driving and distinctiveness thanks to a vast range of accessories and option packs.

It's certainly easy to use around town, thanks to good visibility and a commanding, but uncomfortable, driving position. Outside urban areas it struggles with vague steering and soggy handling. The shape is meant to give improved interior space, but only headroom is remarkable in its generosity.

Best All-Rounder: Wagon R 1.2 GL

Body styles
Estate

Engine capacity
1.0, 1.2

Price from
£7,400

Manufactured in
Japan

Suzuki Baleno

Suzuki has always had a little difficulty convincing buyers that it makes family cars like the Baleno. Small hatchbacks and off-roaders, yes, but its credibility falls away in the mainstream market. But the Baleno is not a bad car, heavily revised for 1999 with a new front end and interior, plus the addition of a diesel engine borrowed from Peugeot.

Performance of the petrol engined cars has always been a strong feature, though the chassis isn't sharp enough to maintain the sporty impression and when the performance is used to the full the engine becomes unrefined and unpleasantly noisy. Space inside isn't brilliant either but comfort levels are good.

Best All-Rounder: Baleno 1.6

Body styles
Saloon, Estate

Engine capacity
1.3, 1.6, 1.8

Price from
£10,500

Manufactured in
Japan

Suzuki Swift

The Suzuki Swift has been around in several forms since 1983, when it was sold as the Geo Metro in the States. A development of that car is still available in the US, now known as the Chevrolet Metro. The original design is Suzuki's though and, several facelifts later, it is being built in Hungary for the Europeans.

With either engine, 'Swift' is something of a contradiction. But interior space is good, it rides well and the car doesn't feel badly built. It's not competitive with the best any more though, so in future its role in developing markets will become more important.

Best All-Rounder: Swift 1.3 GLX

Body styles
Hatchback

Engine capacity
1.0, 1.3

Price from
£6,900

Manufactured in
Hungary

Suzuki Grand Vitara *new!*

With arguably the most pleasing styling of any of the junior off-roader set, there is a degree of purpose to the Grand Vitara that Suzuki has never achieved earlier. Launched as a long-wheelbase five-door with a V6 engine, 1999 sees a short wheelbase version as well as an expanded engine range.

The 2.5 V6 is smooth and refined, pulling well at low speeds as well as when driven enthusiastically. The driving position and front seats give good support too, so this is quite a driver's car for a 4x4. But room in the back seats is tight and boot space is so-so. And that suspension can get too firm for comfort.

Best All-Rounder Grand Vitara V6 5dr

Body styles
Estate

Engine capacity
2.0, 2.5V6, 2.0TD

Price from
£14,000 (est)

Manufactured in
Japan

toyota

Toyota

Third largest car manufacturer in the world, Toyota's enormous model range covers almost every possibility, from family car to sports car to off-roader to the advanced Prius. The Camry is America's best selling car, but while the quality of the product can be in little doubt, Toyota's need for its models to be built for world markets means that many of its cars lack, for example, a European feel to them. But the company has addressed this problem to an extent. Its mainstream family car, the Avensis, is built in the UK, and the forthcoming Yaris will be its first car specifically designed for Europe.

Toyota Prius   *new!*

Toyota's new Prius is the world first production hybrid vehicle using the combination of a 1.5-litre petrol engine and an electric motor to provide one-tenth of the emissions of a normal car. Since going on sale in Japan in December last year, Toyota has upped production to 2000 units per month to cope with the high demand.

The four-door saloon will be capable of 60mpg and an average range of 600 miles when it goes on sale in Europe in 2000. Using its 1.5-litre engine linked to a CVT gearbox, the Prius uses regenerative braking to charge its batteries and switches between petrol or electric power or a combination of the two depending on the driver's needs.

Best All-Rounder: Too early to tell

Body styles Saloon
Engine capacity 1.5
Price from n.a.
Manufactured in Japan

Toyota Corolla

The smiling face of latest Corolla may be more distinctive than before, but beneath the surface it retains many of the previous model's components. That means 1.3 and 1.6-litre petrol engines, a 2.0-litre diesel and four body styles: three & five-door hatchbacks, a saloon and an estate.

As you'd expect, the Corolla is competent in all areas. The airy but drably-trimmed cabin is effective, the engines are reliable, equipment levels are competitive and it's comfortable and easy to drive. In fact, there's nothing much wrong with the car, it's just that more recent competitors have moved the game on to another level.

Best All-Rounder: Corolla 1.6 GS

Body styles
Hatchback, Saloon, Estate

Engine capacity
1.3, 1.6, 2.0D

Price from
£10,000

Manufactured in
Japan, UK

Toyota Starlet

The smallest Toyota is the runt of a large pack, going largely unnoticed in the face of bigger and better cars. Most countries get just a 1.3-litre engine though there is also a 1.5-litre diesel as well as a manic 1.3-litre turbo producing 135bhp.

To drive, the Starlet is much like other Toyotas: easy. All the controls are light, the standard 1.3-litre engine is quiet, the ride is compliant and refinement all round is good. Interior space in the rear is only average though and there is not a lot of fun to be had. But that won't bother owners who are more likely to appreciate its reliability and ease of use.

Best All-Rounder: Starlet 1.3

Body styles
Hatchback

Engine capacity
1.3, 1.3 turbo, 1.5

Price from
£8,000

Manufactured in
Japan

Toyota Camry

Toyota's executive saloon has always struggled to compete with the big players from the prestige marques and with the new small Lexus due before long, the Camry is likely to come under even more pressure. The Toyota may not have the badge or upmarket interior of some of its rivals, but it boasts a roomy interior and several other attributes.

For one there's a long standard equipment list and a choice of two well-refined engines - a 2.2-litre 16v or 3.0-litre V6. The latter is the smoother of the two but ultimately the Camry falls down on its image and anonymous looks despite being a big seller in world markets such as the US and Japan.

Best All-Rounder: Camry V6

Body styles
Saloon

Engine capacity
2.2, 3.0V6

Price from
£20,000

Manufactured in
Japan

Toyota Avensis

The Avensis' predecessors, a whole host of Carinas, always had virtues of fabulous reliability and of being easy company. Fine for those who buy a car along the lines of a washing machine, but ultimately rather dull. The Avensis, however, looks different, with svelte looks and high-pressure marketing behind it.

In reality, though, the status quo is retained. The Avensis is calmly efficient. Its engines are refined, offering good economy and power and the chassis is tuned for smooth comfort, not overtly sporting dynamism. Equipment levels, interior space and build quality are as generously offered as ever too. It is just not a car to raise the pulse rate.

Body styles
Hatchback, Saloon, Estate

Engine capacity
1.6, 1.8, 2.0, 2.0TD

Price from
£14,000

Manufactured in
England

Best All-Rounder: Avensis 2.0 GLS

Toyota MR2

Despite the recent plethora of coupes to enter the market, the aging Toyota MR2 still manages to turn heads on the high street. The baby Ferrari comes in either GT form with a steel roof or as a T-Bar with twin removable roof panels which are stored in the boot behind the mid-mounted engine.

With a highly-tuned 2.0-litre engine producing 168bhp sitting just behind your shoulder, the MR2 still manages to make your spine tingle with superb feedback through the steering and a stubby gearlever that's easy to flick through the gears. The interior may be a little cramped and compromised and the price no longer as competitive as it once was, but the MR2 can still provide plenty of thrills.

Body styles
Coupe

Engine capacity
2.0, 2.0 turbo, 2.2

Price from
£22,000

Manufactured in
Japan

Best All-Rounder: MR2 GT

Toyota Picnic

Quite apart from its unusual name, Toyota's baby MPV has struggled to make an impact against the massive success of its headline-grabbing arch rival, the Renault Scenic. The Picnic may not offer the same level of interior seating flexibility as the Scenic, but it now has seven seats and most models have standard anti-lock brakes and air conditioning.

Two engines are available with the Picnic, a 2.0-litre 126bhp petrol or a 2.2-litre turbo-diesel with 86bhp. In GL and GX forms, the petrol unit also offers the choice of a US-style steering column-mounted automatic like the Previa. It is a good choice for those looking for a compact MPV.

Body styles
MPV

Engine capacity
2.0, 2.2TD

Price from
£16,000

Manufactured in
Japan

Best All-Rounder: Picnic 2.0 GL

Toyota Celica

Like the MR2, Toyota's Celica has suffered from the recent flurry of activity in the coupe market, being overtaken by more modern, and cheaper, competition. Three versions are available, a 1.8 ST with 114bhp and a GT and Cabriolet both powered by the same 2.0-litre 168bhp as in the MR2.

The Cabriolet is massively expensive sitting on the wrong side of £30,000, while even the GT's price tag looks a little steep against younger rivals. While lacking the GT's performance, the entry-level ST represents the better value with a reasonable price as well as the usual Celica traits of a high equipment level and good road manners.

Body styles
Coupe, Convertible

Engine capacity
1.8, 2.0, 2.0 turbo

Price from
£19,300

Manufactured in
Japan

Best All-Rounder: Celica 1.8 ST

Toyota Previa

With the arrival of the Chrysler Grand Voyager and Renault's Grand Espace, Toyota's huge Previa is no longer the only people-carrier on the market that can claim to accommodate seven or eight people and their luggage too. How you view the Previa's sheer size and its single sliding rear door on the nearside only, is a matter of personal choice.

Offered with just a single engine, the performance from the 2.5-litre 133bhp petrol hides the Previa's dimensions well, although its handling can't camouflage the fact that the Toyota is not a small car. That size is a bonus for carrying capacity though, and combined with the excellent build quality can make the Previa a practical and shrewd choice.

Best All-Rounder: Previa GL

Body styles
MPV

Engine capacity
2.4, 2.2TD

Price from
£19,900

Manufactured in
Japan

Toyota Landcruiser Colorado

In the Landcruiser Colorado, Toyota finally has a car to go head-to-head in the mud-slinging stakes with the Mitsubishi Shogun and Land Rover Discovery. Running alongside its larger Amazon stablemate, the Landcruiser twins are underlining Toyota's reputation as a major player in the off-road market.

Available as a three or five-door, most of the models in the Colorado range are powered by a 3.0-litre turbodiesel, although the flagship five-door VX also offers a thirsty 3.4-litre V6. The turbo-diesel five-door is the best of the bunch with two optional rear seats in the boot for further practicality, although the interior is disappointingly plain. A good level of equipment and permanent four-wheel-drive mean the Colorado is equally at home on road or mud-track.

Best All-Rounder: Colorado GX TD 5dr

Body styles
Estate

Engine capacity
2.7, 3.4V6, 3.0TD

Price from
£21,000

Manufactured in
Japan

Toyota RAV4

Just as Suzuki's Samurai did in the 1980s, Toyota's RAV4 single-handedly changed everyone's view of how an off-roader should drive. As enjoyable as a hot hatch, the RAV4 has had a recent refresh to help it compete with the likes of the Freelander and Honda CR-V.

Now available in soft-top form, joining the three and five-door bodystyles, all models are powered by a sporty 2.0-litre engine with GX and VX models getting standard anti-lock brakes and powerful air conditioning. The GX three-door gets removable roof panels, while the soft-top's roof is complicated and awkward to fold and the longer-wheelbase five-door offers improved interior space.

Best All-Rounder: RAV4 GX 3dr

Body styles
Estate, Convertible

Engine capacity
2.0

Price from
£15,000

Manufactured in
Japan

Toyota Landcruiser Amazon *new!*

Just when you thought off-roaders couldn't get any bigger, Toyota has put its flagship 4x4, the Landcruiser Amazon, on steroids. Larger than its predecessor, everything about the Amazon is huge. Available as a seven seater, the boot-mounted seats may be cramped, but they fold up against the side when not in use. The tailgate is split, Range Rover-style.

Engine choice is between a 232bhp 4.7-litre V8 petrol unit with crippling fuel consumption or a 4.2-litre turbo-diesel offering a marginally better 25mpg average. While lacking the Range Rover's image, the Amazon more than makes up with a huge list of standard equipment and, by comparison, a bargain price tag.

Best All-Rounder: Amazon VX TD

Body styles
Estate

Engine capacity
4.7V8, 4.2TD

Price from
£36,800

Manufactured in
Japan

TVR

TVR has won the battle with Lotus to become Britain's most popular sports car manufacturer, helped by its willingness to produce an ever-more outrageous line-up of models to satisfy a loyal band of buyers. The three mainstream models - Chimaera, Griffith and Cerbera - will be joined in 1999 by the stunning Speed Twelve and the mouth-watering Tuscan Speed Six. The Speed Twelve is a £150,000 7.7-litre V12 coupe. It will produce 800bhp - 170bhp more than a McLaren F1! The Tuscan Speed Six looks a little like the Griffith, but uses a new 350bhp straight-six engine. Can TVR do no wrong?

TVR Cerbera

Arguably the best looking TVR, the long, low Cerbera coupe is even wilder inside, with the instruments attached beneath the steering wheel spokes. It is a four seater of sorts, with a chance of squeezing a couple of youngsters in the back.

But the real point of the Cerbera is not the space but the performance. The in-house V8 provides enough power to out-accelerate a Porsche 911 Turbo, making it the fastest and most powerful TVR of them all. There is a chassis to match, but it takes a brave (or foolish) man to exploit the full envelope of Cerbera's possibilities.

Cerbera

TVR Chimaera

This is the slightly softer, more practical TVR for those who find the Griffith a touch too extreme. Yet everything is relative, because the Chimaera still packs an enormous punch from any of its V8 engines. Yet it is an easier car to drive over challenging roads and there's slightly more room inside.

The Chimaera cannot match the likes of Mercedes-Benz for build quality, but it is nonetheless a well-sorted machine, with a reasonably comfortable ride and a hood mechanism that works just fine. That said the Chimaera is no car for the uncommitted, with a heavy clutch and gearchange, and steering that needs the optional power assistance.

Chimaera

TVR Griffith

TVR has yet to surpass the design of the Griffith, a combination of sheer beauty and concealed brutality. It is the least compromised of an uncompromising line-up. Powered by the 5.0-litre version of the Rover V8, it produces 340 bhp, enough to place it in serious supercar league.

Inside there's luxury, with the tight-fitting cockpit trimmed in high quality leather. The controls are uniformly heavy but that's quickly forgotten when the throttle is pressed and the deep, evil rumble curls from the exhausts. The chassis may be good, but ultimately such power in a lightweight car, without traction control and in a relatively short wheelbase, is never going to be for the faint-hearted.

Body styles Chimaera and Griffith: Convertible; Cerbera: Coupe
Engine capacity Chimaera: 4.0V8, 4.5V8, 5.0V8; Griffith: 5.0V8; Cerbera: 4.2V8, 4.5V8
Price from: Chimaera: £31,700; Griffith: £35,700; Cerbera: £41,100
Manufactured in all cars: England

Griffith

Vauxhall/Opel

Vauxhall and Opel are part of the giant General Motors. GM is the largest car manufacturer in the world, although Vauxhall traditionally has had to settle for second place behind Ford in the UK. Opel is the brand name used in other European markets - the cars are identical apart from the badge. The range is currently stable, with the only change being a revised Frontera in late 1998, and the Zafira in Spring 1999, a seven-seater based upon Astra underpinnings.

Vauxhall /Opel Astra   *new!*

   With chassis tuning by Lotus, one of the largest estate bodyshells in its class and a range of new or revised engines, the Astra has at last come into it prime. The present three and five-door hatchback and five-door estate body styles will, in time, be joined by a four-door saloon, a coupe to replace the Calibra and a Renault Scenic-rival called the Zafira.

   There's a full range of engines ranging from a 1.4 up to 1.8-litre 16v and two turbo-diesels. This will be expanded at the end of 1998 by a 1.2 and a 136bhp 2.0-litre that will find its way into a hot hatch model. It is a good car to travel in and an enjoyable one to drive, though the interior design can't compete with the high levels set by the new VW Golf.
Best All-Rounder: Astra 1.6 LS 5dr

Body styles
Hatchback, Saloon, Estate
Engine capacity
1.4, 1.6, 1.8, 2.0, 1.7TD, 2.0TD
Price from
£11,900
Manufactured in
Worldwide

Vauxhall/Opel Vectra

Despite some bad press on its arrival, the only way to judge the Vauxhall Vectra's success is to look in the car park of any motorway service station. There, among the mass of Mondeos, 406s and Primeras, you will find an absolute plethora of Luton's finest in its saloon, hatchback and estate bodystyles.

The Vectra has lots to offer from a roomy interior to a full range of engines from a 1.6 up to a 2.5-litre 168bhp V6 including a pair of turbo-diesels. Vauxhall has also tackled criticisms of the Vectra's dull-driving experience with a new flagship GSi model powered by a 190bhp V6 engine and with lowered suspension and a sporty body kit.

Best All-Rounder: Vectra 1.8 GLS 5dr

Body styles
Hatchback, Saloon, Estate

Engine capacity
1.6, 1.8, 2.0, 2.5V6, 2.0TD

Price from
£14,600

Manufactured in
Germany, UK, Belgium, Turkey

Vauxhall/Opel Tigra

While being based on the run of the mill Corsa, Vauxhall's Tigra had the baby coupe market pretty much to itself until the Ford Puma arrived to spoil the party. Though the Tigra had all the dramatic looks and style of a coupe, it was beaten hands-down for driver involvement by the model from the blue oval.

Offered with either a 1.4 or 1.6 engine (the former available also as an auto), the Tigra's interior is cramped both for taller adults in the front seats and anyone but small children in the rear. It can be fun in a simple, undemanding sort of way, but there is no getting away from the fact that the Puma is by far the more competent all-rounder.

Best All-Rounder: Tigra 1.4

Body styles
Coupe

Engine capacity
1.4, 1.6

Price from
£13,200

Manufactured in
Spain

Vauxhall/Opel Corsa

The Corsa has been around a good few years now, with even its facelift was a couple of years past. So it is a car that is going through the latter stages of its life, and Vauxhall/ Opel have been unable to keep the pot boiling in the way Ford has so impressively with its Fiesta rival.

But it is a practical car, with two body styles, the three-door being distinctive and fun while the five-door has a slightly more sober and practical design. Either way the shape results in a roomy interior boasting comfortable seats and a natural, easy driving position. If the Corsa was more refined and better to drive, things would look a lot better.

Best All-Rounder: Corsa 1.4-16v GLS

Body styles
Past

Engine capacity
1.0, 1.2, 1.4, 1.6, 1.7D, 1.5TD

Price from
£8,500

Manufactured in
Spain

1
2
4

Vauxhall/Opel Omega

Although lacking the prestige and perceived quality of an Audi or BMW, Vauxhall and Opel's executive cruiser has an abundance of ability and a fine feel of solidity. The range of saloons and estates is offered with 2.0, 2.5 or 3.0 petrol engines or an excellent BMW 2.5-litre turbo-diesel. All perform extremely well and, despite the car's size, deliver good economy.

The Omega is also good to drive. Smooth and refined, it has a superbly absorbent ride and an extremely well-balanced chassis that will indulge a keen driver without compromising comfort. An extremely roomy interior with excellent seating completes the picture.

Best All-Rounder: Omega 2.5 V6

Body styles
Saloon, Estate

Engine capacity
2.0, 2.5V6, 3.0V6, 2.5TD

Price from
£19,300

Manufactured in
Germany

Vauxhall/Opel Sintra

Vauxhall's Sintra prides itself on being more like a car to drive than the traditional people-carriers; that's certainly true of its looks and driving position if not its road manners. Arriving considerably later to the MPV fray hasn't given the Vauxhall any advantages either with poor sales that can't hope to compete with the Ford Galaxys and VW Sharans of this world.

The limited engine range hasn't helped, with a choice between 2.2-litre 16v or a 3.0-litre petrol units, but a new 2.2 turbo-diesel option arrives for 1999. The Sintra's interior packaging is not the best, but there are sliding doors to aid access to the rear and a high level of equipment as standard.

Best All-Rounder: Sintra 2.2 CD

Body styles
MPV

Engine capacity
2.2, 3.0V6, 2.2TD

Price from
£19,450

Manufactured in
US

Vauxhall/Opel Monterey

While the Monterey's twin sister, the Isuzu Trooper, has just undergone some major revisions, the Vauxhall offering continues in its original (and dated) guise. Very capable off road, the Monterey is available as either a three-door or as a longer-wheelbase five-door, the latter offered with an optional third row of folding seats.

Engine choice is restricted to a 3.2-litre petrol V6 or a 3.1-litre turbo-diesel and both combine well with the Monterey's excellent off-roading characteristics, though neither is particularly refined. Equipment levels are high with twin airbags, anti-lock brakes and a CD player fitted to all models but, like the outside styling, the interior is now showing its age.

Best All-Rounder: Monterey 3.1 TDS 5dr

Body styles
Estate

Engine capacity
3.2V6, 3.1TD

Price from
£25,700

Manufactured in
Japan

Vauxhall/Opel Frontera   *new!*

Despite its size and dated interior, Vauxhall's Frontera has managed to succeed in the off-roader market, relatively speaking, where other big names have failed, notably Ford's Maverick. But big changes for 1999 have seen the Frontera's rugged good looks subtly improved, with a whole host of other changes.

Engine choice has been widened with the option of 2.2-litre or 3.2 V6 petrol engines or a new 2.2-litre turbo-diesel from Vauxhall's ECOTEC family; an automatic is also now available for the first time. Other changes beneath the skin have seen the Frontera's road manners improved for less road and wind noise and better ride and handling.

Best All-Rounder: Frontera 2.2 TD

Body styles
Estate, Convertible

Engine capacity
2.0, 3.2V6, 2.2TD

Price from
£16,500 (est)

Manufactured in
England

Venturi 300 Atlantique

France's fastest production car gains twin turbo-chargers in place of the single unit for 1999, a mild cosmetic face-lift and the option of a non-turbo automatic transmission model. It all adds up to a supercar in the true sense, rivalling Lotus in terms of performance although yet to establish its credentials strongly in non-French markets.

Underneath that composite bodywork is a complex semi-monocoque steel chassis which provides huge reserves of grip - the Venturi is a very forgiving car to drive fast. But it is surprisingly luxurious too - more so than most competitors - with deep carpets, walnut trim and leather. Do not dismiss the Venturi too quickly.

Best All-Rounder: Atlantique Twin Turbo

Body styles	Price from
Coupe	£60,000

Engine capacity	Manufactured in
3.0, 3.0 twin-turbo	France

Westfield

What started as a replica of Caterham's Seven was forced, by legislation, to develop its own image and direction. Even so, comparisons between the two are inevitable as key particulars have remained: the Westfield is a lightweight, front-engined, rear-drive two seater with stunning performance and terrible wet-weather protection.

Most Westfields use Ford powerplants, the exception being the SEiGHT which gets a V8 from the Range Rover. Freed from pulling two tonnes of off-road metal, it makes for eye-popping acceleration. But even the lesser-powered versions are genuinely quick with the advantage of pin-sharp handling.

Best All-Rounder: Westfield 1800

Body styles	Price from
Convertible	£13,300

Engine capacity	Manufactured in
1.6, 1.8, 3.9V8	UK

Volkswagen

Volkswagen

With the loss of the Corrado coupe it looked like Volkswagen was going through one of its boring phases, concentrating on solid, dependable, family cars. That, of course, has always been one of VW's core values, but once more there is a sense of excitement about the brand. The new Beetle reaches Europe in late 1998, the UK a year later. The Lupo, a sub-Polo hatchback, is the same as a Seat Arosa beneath the skin, but has more dynamic styling. The Bora is a Golf-derived saloon that eschews the pipe smoking image of the earlier Vento and Jetta for a sporting stance to compete with the BMW 3-Series. Things are looking good.

Bora

VW Golf   *new!*

While on the surface the new Golf may not look all that different from its predecessor, it is in reality totally new. While the old estate model continues for the time being, the Bora four-door saloon derivative of the new hatch replaces the Vento next year and the cabriolet has had a facelift to give it the looks of the new model.

Many of the engines are familiar from other VW Group products, and the GTi models now get a choice of either a new 2.3-litre V5 engine, 1.8, 1.8 turbo or 1.9 turbo-diesel. The interior is where the new Golf has made the biggest impact however, and the faultless build quality and good level of equipment takes the class levels one step further.

Best All-Rounder: Golf 1.6S 5dr

Body styles
Hatchback
Engine capacity
1.4, 1.6, 1.8, 1.8 turbo, 2.3V5, 2.8V6, 1.9D, 1.9TD
Price from
£12,300
Manufactured in
Germany

VW Polo

The most noticeable evidence of the parts sharing that is becoming increasing common within the Volkswagen Group can be seen in the Polo, which has a great deal in common with Seat's Ibiza and Cordoba. While the hatchbacks have enough differences to look like separate models, the Polo estate and saloon are no more than re-badged version of the equivalent Cordobas.

That, of course, doesn't stop the Polo being a good car. Its interior has a solid (if sombre) feel lacking from rivals - particularly Oriental and French ones - and interior space is competitive. The range of engines is wide enough to please most and refinement is excellent too. The Polo may not be the most fun in its class, but its maturity provides good compensation.

Best All-Rounder: Polo 1.6 CL

Body styles
Hatchback, Saloon, Estate

Engine capacity
1.0, 1.4, 1.6, 1.7D, 1.9D, 1.9TD

Price from
£8,300

Manufactured in
Germany, Spain

VW Beetle

Herbie is back! The lovable Volkswagen Beetle has made a return, although due to massive success in the USA where long waiting lists have built up, it looks unlikely to arrive in Europe before late 1999. With a choice of 2.0-litre petrol or 1.9-litre turbo-diesel power, the engine is ahead of the driver and powers the front wheels, the result of the car's Golf underpinnings.

The Beetle's three-door hatchback bodystyle is familiar, with interior space compromised by that curving roof line making for an odd driving position far back in the cabin and cramped rear seats. Nice touches include a dash-mounted flower vase and unusual indigo back-lit instruments.

Best All-Rounder: Beetle 2.0

Body styles
Hatchback

Engine capacity
2.0, 1.9TD

Price from
£14,000 (est)

Manufactured in
Mexico

VW Sharan

Volkswagen joined forces with Ford to develop this MPV, also sold as the Ford Galaxy as well as the Seat Alhambra. It is among the most stylish and easy to drive of this type of car, with a good looking, well-thought-out interior, though like many it fails to provide sufficient luggage space with seven seats in use.

The Sharan's engine range offers something for everybody, though the 2.0-litre petrol and quite noisy 1.9-litre 90bhp turbo-diesel have to work hard in this big vehicle. Better are the more powerful 110bhp turbo-diesel and the 1.8-litre petrol turbo - lively yet quiet and refined.

Best All-Rounder: Sharan TDi 110

Body styles
MPV

Engine capacity
1.8, 1.8 turbo, 2.0, 2.8V6, 1.9TD

Price from
£18,600

Manufactured in
Portugal

VW Golf

Volkswagen's Golf convertible and estate continue to be sold in the previous, Mark 3, form. The thinking behind this is two-fold. Sales of these niche models are not really high enough to justify re-engineering the new Mark 4 Golf into additional body styles, while buyers seemed to be prepared, for a while at least, to accept second best.

Not that buyers will necessarily realise. The Golf Convertible recently underwent a nose job that makes it look uncannily like the more modern hatchback. But even so, the cabriolet remains a strong contender in its class, well built and dependable. The estate is less competitive, and will be dropped by early 1999.

Best All-Rounder: Cabriolet 2.0

Body styles	**Price from**
Estate, Convertible	Estate £12,800
	Convertible £15,600
Engine capacity	
1.4, 1.6, 1.8, 2.0, 2.8V6,	**Manufactured in**
1.9D, 1.9TD	Germany

VW Passat

In one single swoop, the VW Passat has gone from being a capable but anonymous also-ran to the top of its class. As you'd expect from a car wearing the VW badge, build quality is first class and the interior, while a little unadventurous, is solid and reasonably stylish.

As before, the Passat is offered as a four-door saloon or a five-door estate, although the latter is not the ultimate luggage-carrier it once was and is beaten in size by some rivals. The VW has a range of engines many of which it shares with the Audi A4 and, as with the Golf, the turbo-diesels are the real headline attractions particularly the 110bhp 1.9 TDI.

Best All-Rounder: Passat TDI 110

Body styles
Saloon, Estate

Engine capacity
1.6, 1.8, 1.8 turbo, 2.0, 2.3V5, 2.8V6, 1.9TDi

Price from
£15,500

Manufactured in
Germany

VW Lupo   *new!*

Following the Volkswagen Group's policy of using the same underpinnings and mechanicals across as many of its four main marques as possible, the new VW Lupo is basically a reworked Seat Arosa with a revised bodyshell and entirely different interior.

The baby Volkswagen will get the same line-up of engines as the Arosa, comprising of the 1.0 and 1.4-litre petrols and 1.7-litre turbo-diesel, although the Lupo will eventually add VW's new 3-cylinder turbo-diesel as well. On sale in Europe at the end of this year, the Lupo won't arrive in the UK until early 1999, but has already starred in a one-make racing series in Germany.

Best All-Rounder: Lupo 1.4

Body styles
Hatchback

Engine capacity
1.0, 1.4, 1.7D

Price from
£8,000

Manufactured in
Germany

VOLVO

Volvo

Has Volvo finally made up its mind what it wants to be? Certainly not a maker of small cars - each decade it has cut out the smallest model in the range. A maker of safe cars? Definitely, but Volvo has discovered that it is not incompatible with building cars that are sporting to drive as well. Every model in the range has a very high performance derivative to complement the cooking models. Volvo is now an enticing proposition for all types of driver, reinforced by the introduction of the new luxury saloon, the S80, in mid-98.

Volvo C70

Having had its debut in a starring role in the film *The Saint* last year, the Volvo C70 coupe will smash any preconceptions you may have had about Volvo in the past. The C70 is stylish and glamorous and has the performance to match.

With a convertible version joining it late in 1998, the present coupe is offered with two engines, a 2.5-litre model with 193bhp and a scorching 240bhp 2.3-litre turbo that will eat most hot hatches for breakfast. With a sizable and luxurious interior, the C70 is also offered with a GT pack that includes leather upholstery, climate control and a 10-speaker stereo system that rivals the Albert Hall for sound quality.

Best All-Rounder: C70 2.5T

Body styles
Coupe, Convertible
Engine capacity
2.5T, 2.3 turbo
Price from
£30,500
Manufactured in
Sweden

Volvo S40/ V40

Volvo has never had much sales success with its smaller cars, although the S40/V40 range built in Holland alongside the Mitsubishi Carisma seems to be rewriting the rule-book somewhat. The V40 estate follows the latest fashion for life-style estates, although can't compete with the big load carriers in the class.

While it is difficult to get emotional the S40/ V40, like it is easy to do with the Audi A4 or BMW 3-Series, the pair are well built and have a fair range of engines to choose from including the frugal Mitsubishi 1.8 GDI unit and the 200bhp turbocharged scorcher in the sporty T4. The huge range of option packs and trim levels can make deciding on your car's final specification a long-term project.

Best All-Rounder: V40 2.0 Turbo

Body styles
Saloon, Estate

Engine capacity
1.6, 1.8, 1.9 turbo, 2.0, 2.0 turbo, 1.9TD

Price from
£14,000

Manufactured in
Netherlands

Volvo S80

This is Volvo's first real attempt to tackle executive contenders from BMW and Mercedes-Benz. The old 960 has its own gawky charm, but this is the car to hit the targets head on. Inside and out the S80 feels like a big car, and with fabulous support from the seats, five can travel in complete comfort.

Naturally it is loaded with safety features, including airbags everywhere and a new anti-whiplash seat system. Engines range from 2.4-litre to a twin-turbo 2.8 six; the 2.9-litre is likely to be a popular choice, producing a refined and willing performance, though the smoothness of the transmission is not perfect.

Best All-Rounder: S80 2.9

Body styles
Saloon

Engine capacity
2.4, 2.8twin turbo, 2.9

Price from
£22,000

Manufactured in
Sweden

Volvo S70/ V70

The Volvo 850 and its S70/ V70 successor is almost single-handedly responsible for the turn-around of Volvo's fortunes in recent years. The latest changes have helped to keep the popular Swede towards the head of the pack with the estate is still the customers' favourite.

The range of five-cylinder engines is capable and very diverse from the Bi-Fuel model which can run on gas to the 240bhp T5 and from numerous four-wheel-drive versions to a superb 2.5-litre turbo-diesel borrowed from Audi. Build quality and interior space are good and the estate is full of clever touches showing that Volvo still hasn't forgotten its core-buyers.

Best All-Rounder: V70 2.5 20v

Body styles
Saloon, Estate

Engine capacity
2.0, 2.0 turbo, 2.3 turbo, 2.5, 2.5TD

Price from
£19,500

Manufactured in
Sweden, Belgium

Aro

We used to know the Aro 10 range as the Dacia Duster, and it hasn't changed much in the ten years since British customers were last offered it. This off-road utility machine is available in a variety of forms: front-wheel drive or four-wheel drive, soft-top or hard-top and with a choice of Renault engines (1.2 and 1.4-litre petrol, 1.9 litre diesel and turbo-diesel). There's also an entry-level Spartana marketed as a fun car.

All models have a very basic feel to them and build quality is notoriously lacking. But the Aro has simplicity, economy and go-anywhere ability on its side.

Pick of the range: 1.9 turbo-diesel

Dacia

The Renault 12 must be qualify as one of the longest-lived models in the world - it's still in production in Romania after 31 years as the Dacia. There are two basic models: the 1310 (sold in saloon and estate forms) and the 1325 (a five-door hatchback - a shape the old Renault 12 was never made in). There are three engine choices: 1.4 and 1.6-litre petrol and 1.6-litre turbo-diesel.

Apart from plastic bumpers, a different grille and an updated interior, the Dacia is virtually identical to the old Renault 12. That means a driving experience more akin to 1969 than 1999.

Pick of the range: 1325 turbo-diesel

FSO Caro

The ancient FSO Polonez is creaking on in production as the Caro. In Britain the Caro is no longer sold but you can still buy one new in France. The base engines are 1.5 or 1.6-litre petrol units, or you can have a Peugeot 1.9-litre diesel. The most popular body style is the five-door hatchback but there is also now a new four-door saloon model called the Atou.

Underneath it all lies the floor-pan of the Fiat 125, a car that has been out of production so long that some people now regard it as a "classic". The engines are frankly the only good things about the Caro, which is hopelessly outdated in all other respects.

Pick of the range: 1.9 diesel

Hindustan Ambassador

Despite increasing competition from more modern cars, the Hindustan Ambassador is still a very popular car in India. Not much has changed since 1954, when it was launched by Morris as the Oxford. The main difference is under the bonnet: there is a 73bhp Isuzu 1.8-litre petrol engine or a choice of 1.5 or 2.0-litre diesels.

The Ambassador is an opportunity to own a brand new slice of the past. It is a massive car compared with today's family transport, but don't expect much sophistication, just enjoy the character and charm. You can buy one in Britain through London-based Fullbore Motors.

Pick of the range: Ambassador 1.8

Lada 2110

Ladas may be a distant memory for British buyers but over half a million cars are still produced in the Russian factory built by Fiat 30 years ago. The 2110 is a relatively new model with distinctive styling, offered in saloon, hatchback and estate forms. As well as 1.5 and 1.5 16V engines, there is a GTi version with a 150bhp 2.0-litre Opel engine and the long wheelbase Konsul limousine with, bizarrely, a 120bhp rotary engine.

In dynamic terms the 2110 falls a long way behind western standards and, although the interiors are much plusher than before, the standard of finish is pretty rough. At least Ladas are built strong enough to withstand a Siberian winter.

Pick of the range: 2110 GTi

Mahindra

Rock bottom prices were not enough to save the Mahindra CJ in Britain. But in India, things are as buoyant as ever. The mainstay of the range is the CJ, basically a licensed version of the American Jeep CJ-3 produced in Bombay since 1949. It is still powered by the ancient wartime 2.2-litre sidevalve engine, or various diesel units including engines from Peugeot. Four different wheelbase lengths are offered, and there is a choice of open or closed bodywork and 2WD or 4WD.

Make no mistake: this is transport at its most painfully basic. The CJ is noisy, slow and hopeless on tarmac. Take it into the rough stuff, though, and it comes into its own.

Pick of the range: Armada 2.5 diesel

Tata Mint

The Indian car industry is growing up - that's the inescapable conclusion when you see Tata's new small car. Styled in Italy by IDEA, with a French-designed engine, the Tata is a little five-door hatchback that promises to give the Fiat Palio a run for its money. Its 1.4-litre engine is offered in petrol and diesel forms, with a 4 or 5-speed transmission.

Excellent packaging means this is a very spacious little car, and the interior is well presented and comfortably equipped. All-independent suspension ensures solid handling and there are some impressive options such as power steering, air conditioning and electric windows.

Pick of the range: 1.4 MPI

Tatra 700

The idiosyncratic Czech car maker Tatra continues to produce its luxury cars, though in steadily decreasing circles (only 24 cars were made in 1997). The 700 model is its latest offering, a four-door saloon offered in two wheelbase lengths and with a technically-interesting 200bhp 3.5-litre V8 quad-cam engine - designed with British help - mounted in the tail. .

Despite the rear-engined layout, handling is not bad and the degree of luxury inside is impressive. This is the sort of car that would appeal to eccentrics and British customers can now buy one from a specialist importer.

Pick of the range: 3.5 EFI

Volkswagen Sedan

VW in Mexico might now be making waves with the new Beetle but to taxi drivers and budget motorists there is still only one car - the good old Beetle (now called simply Sedan). It's cheap, reliable, easy to service and of course much loved.

These days the old Beetle has some decidedly new features, like fuel injection, catalyst and disc brakes. The 1.6-litre flat four engine is still air-cooled, pumping out a modest 44bhp. Several companies have begun importing Sedans to the UK but VW has warned against them, saying the old Beetle falls far short of modern expectations.

Pick of the range: 1.6i

Volkswagen Gol

Brazil may have lost the World Cup final but it has scored a winner with the Gol (which means 'goal' in Portuguese). It is Brazil's best-selling car, offering a wide range of body styles - 3/5-door hatchback, 3/5-door estate (dubbed the Parati), and five engines: a tax-break 54bhp 1.0-litre, a 94bhp 1.6, a 105bhp 1.8 and two 2.0-litre engines with 111bhp or, in GTi form, 145bhp. Alcohol fuel is an option.

The Gol is an all-Brazilian design resembling a scaled-down Golf. It is a modern car in all respects, with a well laid-out cabin, five-speed transmission and front disc brakes.

Pick of the range: 2.0 GTi 16V

Yugo Koral

Ever since the Balkan crisis the British market has missed out on the Yugo, but it's still made by a factory that also churns out weapons and agricultural machinery. Now called the Koral, the three-door hatchback Yugo sits right at the bottom of the market. It is offered with a choice of 903cc, 1116cc and 1302cc engines, all Fiat-derived.

Being based on the antediluvian Fiat 127, you can't expect anything other than a crude ride. In all respects - packaging, fit and finish, equipment, engineering - it is so far off the pace that it really ought to be put out to pasture.

Pick of the range: Koral 1.3

Zaz Tavria

From a position as the second-biggest car maker in Russia, ZAZ has plunged into abject crisis under Ukrainian rule - a mere 1190 cars were produced in 1997. The Tavria is a small hatchback, offered in 1102 (three-door) and 1105 (five-door forms). There's a choice of engines too: a 1.1-litre unit with either fuel injection or a carburettor, and a 1.3-litre.

This is family car transport at its most basic. It is surely the cheapest car sold anywhere (at one stage UK imports were planned at below £4000), and that is reflected in its ultra-basic specification. Still, it is rugged enough to deal with very harsh local road conditions.

Pick of the range: 1102 1.3

Want to know the hard facts behind the catalogue entries? The tables on the next nine pages give the technical background to cars listed in the Guide.

By and large we have used the car manufacturers' own figures, so in places where they are unable or unwilling to release the information we have placed a dash. American car makers are notoriously reluctant even to say how fast their cars are!

Engine capacity is given in cubic centimetres, power in bhp, although the common metric power unit, PS, gives much the same result. Fuel type is denoted by P for petrol, D for diesel. Engine configuration is a combination of the layout and the number of cylinders - S equates to straight (or in-line), F for flat (or horizontally opposed) V is self explanatory; the number of cylinders follows. The driven wheels are noted, Front, Rear or 4 wheel drive. Top speed and acceleration from rest to 60 mph are the two universally popular measures of a car's performance. Just one fuel consumption figure is given, the combined cycle, as this is arguably the most realistic of the statutory tests. The insurance group is the standardised rating system used in the UK, on a scale of 1 to 20. Groups cannot be given for cars not sold in the UK, or the very latest models which have yet to be rated. Length and width are for the saloon or hatchback version, with two figures given where there is a discrepancy between models. Figures for estate cars are not included, and the weight, in kilograms, is for the lightest version in each range.

Finally, not all the cars listed will be available for sale in the UK. Check the new price tables later on for the definitive list of availability, then cross refer back to this list. Remember that some cars are sold only in a restricted model range in the UK, and different examples are available elsewhere - the data table is as complete as we can make it.

	Engine cc	Power bhp	Fuel	Engine config.	Driven wheels	Top Speed mph	0-60mph secs	MPG average	Insurance group	Length mm	Width mm	Weight kg
AC												
Ace	4942	345	P	V8	R	165	5.7	23	20	4420	1870	1510
Superblower	4942	355	P	V8	R	165	4.2	18	20	4200	1746	1120
ALFA ROMEO												
145												
1.4 Twin Spark	1370	102	P	S4	F	115	11.2	35	-	4095	1710	1135
1.6 Twin Spark	1599	120	P	S4	F	121	10.2	34	11	4095	1710	1165
1.8 Twin Spark	1747	140	P	S4	F	127	9.2	34	13	4095	1710	1195
2.0 Cloverleaf	1969	150	P	S4	F	130	8.4	32	14	4095	1710	1240
146												
1.4 Twin Spark	1370	102	P	S4	F	116	11.5	35	-	4255	1710	1160
1.6 Twin Spark	1599	120	P	S4	F	122	10.5	34	11	4255	1710	1190
1.8 Twin Spark	1747	140	P	S4	F	129	9.4	34	13	4255	1710	1215
2.0 ti	1969	150	P	S4	F	130	8.5	34	14	4255	1710	1275
156												
1.6 Twin Spark	1599	120	P	S4	F	125	10.5	34	-	4430	1750	1230
1.8 Twin Spark	1747	144	P	S4	F	129	9.3	34	11	4430	1750	1230
2.0 Twin Spark	1969	155	P	S4	F	134	8.6	33	14	4430	1750	1250
2.5	2492	190	P	V6	F	142	7.3	25	16	4430	1750	1320
1.9 JTD	1910	105	D	S4	F	117	10.5	48	-	4430	1750	1270
2.4 JTD	2387	136	D	S5	F	126	9.5	42	-	4430	1750	1350
166												
2.0 Twin Spark	1969	144	P	S4	F	-	-	-	-	4720	1810	-
2.0 Turbo	1997	200	P	V6	F	-	-	-	-	4720	1810	-
2.5	2492	190	P	V6	F	-	-	-	-	4720	1810	-
3.0	2959	226	P	V6	F	-	-	-	-	4720	1810	-
2.4 JTD	2387	136	D	S5	F	-	-	-	-	4720	1810	-
Spider												
2.0 Twin Spark	1969	155	P	S4	F	130	8.4	30	17	4285	1780	1370
3.0	2959	192	P	V6	F	141	7.3	22	-	4285	1780	1420
GTV												
2.0 Twin Spark	1969	155	P	S4	F	133	8.4	30	16	4285	1780	1370
2.0 Turbo	1996	200	P	V6	F	147	7.2	24	-	4285	1780	1430
3.0	2959	226	P	V6	F	149	6.7	19	-	4285	1780	1415
ARO												
10												
1.4	1397	63	P	S4	4X4	75	-	25	-	3835	1645	1120
1.9 D	1870	64	D	S4	4X4	81	-	28	-	3835	1645	1285
1.9 TD	1870	94	D	S4	4X4	97	-	23	-	3835	1645	1635
ASTON MARTIN												
DB7	3239	335	P	S6	R	165	5.7	18	20	4646	1240	1700
V8	5430	355	P	V8	R	155	5.8	14	20	4745	1944	1950
Vantage	5430	557	P	V8	R	186	4.6	13	20	4745	1944	1990
AUDI												
A3												
1.6	1595	101	P	S4	F	117	11.3	37	9	4152	1735	1090
1.8	1781	125	P	S4	F	126	10.1	33	12	4152	1735	1140
1.8 Turbo	1781	150	P	S4	F	135	8.1	36	16	4152	1735	1145
1.9 TD	1896	90	D	S4	F	112	12.6	55	-	4152	1735	1170
1.9 TD	1896	110	D	S4	F	120	10.5	57	10	4152	1735	1170
A4												
1.6	1595	101	P	S4	F	119	11.9	36	10	4480	1735	1185
1.8	1781	125	P	S4	F	127	10.5	33	13	4480	1735	1240
1.8 Turbo	1781	150	P	S4	F	140	8.3	36	15	4480	1735	1270
2.4	2393	165	P	V6	F	140	8.2	28	15	4480	1735	1275
2.4 quattro	2393	165	P	V6	4X4	136	8.4	27	-	4480	1735	1380
2.8	2771	193	P	V6	F	149	7.3	27	17	4480	1735	1285
2.8 quattro	2771	193	P	V6	4X4	148	7.3	26	17	4480	1735	1400
2.7 Turbo S4	2671	265	P	V6	4X4	155	5.6	25	-	4480	1735	1510
1.9 TD	1896	90	D	S4	F	114	13.3	50	12	4480	1735	1240
1.9 TD 110	1896	110	D	S4	F	122	11.3	57	13	4480	1735	1240
1.9 TD 110 quattro	1896	110	D	S4	4X4	122	11.3	-	13	4480	1735	1385
2.5 TD	2496	150	D	V6	F	138	9.0	41	-	4480	1735	1355
A6												
1.8	1781	125	P	S4	F	126	11.3	33	-	4795	1810	1320
1.8 Turbo	1781	150	P	S4	F	135	9.4	34	14	4795	1810	1355
2.6	2598	165	P	V6	F	138	9.1	29	15	4795	1810	1400
2.8	2771	193	P	V6	F	147	8.1	29	17	4795	1810	1420
2.8 quattro	2771	193	P	V6	4X4	145	7.9	26	17	4795	1810	1575
1.9 TD 110	1896	110	D	S4	F	120	12.3	50	13	4795	1810	1365
2.5 TD	2496	150	D	V6	F	135	9.7	41	-	4795	1810	1520
A8												
2.8	2771	193	P	V6	F	140	10.2	25	18	5035	1880	1510

AUDI cont'd

	Engine cc	Power bhp	Fuel	Engine config.	Driven wheels	Top Speed mph	0-60mph secs	MPG average	Insurance group	Length mm	Width mm	Weight kg
3.7	3697	230	P	V8	F	153	8.7	24	19	5035	1880	1645
4.2	4172	299	P	V8	F	155	7.1	21	20	5035	1880	1750
4.2 quattro	4172	340	P	V8	4X4	155	7.3	21	20	5035	1880	1720
2.5 TD	2496	150	D	V6	F	132	11.3	32	-	5035	1880	1595
TT												
1.8 T	1781	180	P	S4	F	140	7.1	35	-	4040	1860	1205
1.8 T quattro	1781	180	P	S4	4X4	138	7.1	32	-	4040	1860	1320
1.8 T quattro	1781	225	P	S4	4X4	151	6.2	31	-	4040	1860	1395
Cabriolet												
1.8	1781	125	P	S4	F	121	11.5	30	17	4366	1695	1370
2.0	1984	116	P	S4	F	116	12.9	29	-	4366	1695	1350
2.6	2598	150	P	V6	F	130	10.2	25	17	4366	1695	1455
2.8	2771	174	P	V6	F	135	9.8	26	17	4366	1695	1455
1.9 TD	1896	90	D	S4	F	109	14.7	47	-	4366	1695	1400

BENTLEY

	Engine cc	Power bhp	Fuel	Engine config.	Driven wheels	Top Speed mph	0-60mph secs	MPG average	Insurance group	Length mm	Width mm	Weight kg
Arnage	4398	350	P	V8	R	150	6.2	17	20	5390	1930	2302
Continental R	6750	385	P	V8	R	155	5.9	16	20	5342	1880	2450
Continental T	6750	426	P	V8	R	170	5.8	11	20	5342	1880	2490
Azure	6750	385	P	V8	R	150	5.9	16	20	5342	1880	2610

BMW

	Engine cc	Power bhp	Fuel	Engine config.	Driven wheels	Top Speed mph	0-60mph secs	MPG average	Insurance group	Length mm	Width mm	Weight kg
3-Series												
316i	1596	102	P	S4	R	117	12.3	37	10	4435	1710	1190
318i 8v	1796	115	P	S4	R	125	11.3	36	11	4435	1710	1205
318i 16v	1895	140	P	S4	R	132	10.2	35	12	4435	1710	1240
320i	1991	150	P	S6	R	133	10.0	32	13	4435	1710	1285
323i	2494	170	P	S6	R	141	8.0	31	15	4435	1710	1310
328i	2793	193	P	S6	R	148	7.3	31	16	4435	1710	1320
M3	3201	321	P	S6	R	155	5.6	25	19	4435	1710	1440
318tds	1665	90	D	S4	R	114	12.0	44	10	4435	1710	1320
325tds	2498	143	D	S6	R	133	10.4	39	14	4435	1710	1320
New 3-Series												
318i	1895	118	P	S4	R	128	10.4	36	-	4470	1740	1285
320i	1991	150	P	S6	R	136	9.9	32	-	4470	1740	1365
323i	2494	170	P	S6	R	143	8.0	31	-	4470	1740	1370
328i	2793	193	P	S6	R	149	7.0	31	-	4470	1740	1470
320d	1951	136	D	S4	R	129	9.9	50	-	4470	1740	1375
5-Series												
520i	1991	150	P	S6	R	138	10.2	31	14	4775	1800	1410
523i	2495	170	P	S6	R	143	8.5	27	15	4775	1800	1420
528i	2793	193	P	S6	R	148	7.5	29	16	4775	1800	1440
535i	3498	235	P	V8	R	154	7.0	24	17	4775	1800	1540
540i	4398	286	P	V8	R	155	6.2	23	18	4775	1800	1585
525tds	2498	143	D	S6	R	132	10.4	37	14	4775	1800	1480
7-Series												
728i	2793	193	P	S6	R	140	9.6	25	17	4985	1860	1670
735i	3498	235	P	V8	R	151	8.4	22	18	4985	1860	1725
740i	4398	286	P	V8	R	155	7.6	22	19	4985	1860	1790
750i	5379	326	P	V12	R	155	6.6	20	20	4985	1860	1995
725tds	2498	143	D	S6	R	128	12.2	36	-	4985	1860	1710
8-Series												
840Ci	4398	286	P	V8	R	155	7.4	16	20	4780	1855	1780
850Ci	5379	326	P	V12	R	155	6.3	-	20	4780	1855	1880
Z3												
1.8	1796	116	P	S4	R	121	10.5	-	-	4025	1690	1150
1.9	1895	140	P	S4	R	128	9.5	35	14	4025	1690	1175
2.8	2793	192	P	S6	R	134	7.4	29	16	4025	1690	1260
M Roadster	3201	321	P	S6	R	155	5.4	24	19	4025	1690	1350

BRISTOL

	Engine cc	Power bhp	Fuel	Engine config.	Driven wheels	Top Speed mph	0-60mph secs	MPG average	Insurance group	Length mm	Width mm	Weight kg
Blenheim	5900	227	P	V8	R	150	6.9	-	20	4870	1750	1745

BUICK

	Engine cc	Power bhp	Fuel	Engine config.	Driven wheels	Top Speed mph	0-60mph secs	MPG average	Insurance group	Length mm	Width mm	Weight kg
Regal												
3.8	3791	205	P	V6	F	121	-	30	-	4983	1847	1560
3.8 S'charged	3791	240	P	V6	F	137	-	28	-	4983	1847	1607

CADILLAC

	Engine cc	Power bhp	Fuel	Engine config.	Driven wheels	Top Speed mph	0-60mph secs	MPG average	Insurance group	Length mm	Width mm	Weight kg
Catera	2962	203	P	V6	R	138	8.5	20	-	4925	1785	1710
Seville												
4.6	4565	275	P	V8	F	131	7.5	20	-	5185	1885	1740
4.6 STS	4565	305	P	V8	F	150	7.5	20	-	5185	1885	1765
Escalade	5733	255	P	V8	4X4	-	-	-	-	5557	1948	2390
Deville												
4.6	4565	279	P	V8	F	112	7.8	-	-	5330	1940	1820

CADILLAC cont'd

	Engine cc	Power bhp	Fuel	Engine config.	Driven wheels	Top Speed mph	0-60mph secs	MPG average	Insurance group	Length mm	Width mm	Weight kg
4.6	4565	305	P	V8	F	130	7.5	-	-	5330	1940	1845

CATERHAM

	Engine cc	Power bhp	Fuel	Engine config.	Driven wheels	Top Speed mph	0-60mph secs	MPG average	Insurance group	Length mm	Width mm	Weight kg
Seven												
1.6 8v	1598	101	P	S4	R	110	6.7	-	-	3380	1575	525
1.6	1588	115	P	S4	R	112	6.2	-	-	3380	1575	550
1.6 Supersport	1588	133	P	S4	R	120	5.7	-	-	3380	1575	550
1.6 Superlight	1588	133	P	S4	R	129	4.6	-	-	3100	1575	490
1.8	1796	124	P	S4	R	118	5.8	-	-	3380	1575	550
1.8 Supersport	1796	140	P	S4	R	122	5.3	-	-	3380	1575	550
1.8 Superlight R	1796	190	P	S4	R	140	4.0	-	-	3100	1575	470
C21												
1.6	1588	115	P	S4	R	119	6.4	-	-	3800	1580	650
1.6 Supersport	1588	133	P	S4	R	131	5.8	-	-	3800	1580	650
1.8	1795	124	P	S4	R	124	6.3	-	-	3800	1580	650
1.8 Supersport	1795	140	P	S4	R	130	5.8	-	-	3800	1580	650
1.8 R	1795	190	P	S4	R	140	5.0	-	-	3800	1580	650

CHEVROLET

	Engine cc	Power bhp	Fuel	Engine config.	Driven wheels	Top Speed mph	0-60mph secs	MPG average	Insurance group	Length mm	Width mm	Weight kg
Camaro												
3.4	3791	200	P	V6	R	125	-	19	-	4910	1885	1500
5.7	5733	285	P	V8	T	150	6.5	14	-	4910	1885	1550
Corvette												
5.7	5733	300	P	V8	R	159	4.9	27	-	4535	1795	1500
5.7	5735	330	P	V8	R	163	4.9	27	-	4535	1795	1500
Malibu												
2.4	2392	152	P	S4	F	112	9.5	30	-	4840	1760	1385
3.1 V6	3135	158	P	V6	F	112	9.0	25	-	4840	1760	1395
Blazer	4300	199	P	V6	R	112	10.1	19	-	4639	1736	1590
Suburban												
5.7	5733	255	P	V8	4X4	-	-	-	-	5557	1948	2390
7.4	7400	290	P	V8	4X4	-	-	-	-	5557	1948	2500

CHRYSLER

	Engine cc	Power bhp	Fuel	Engine config.	Driven wheels	Top Speed mph	0-60mph secs	MPG average	Insurance group	Length mm	Width mm	Weight kg
Neon												
1.8	1796	116	P	S4	F	120	11.1	37	7	4365	1715	1150
2.0	1996	132	P	S4	F	125	8.8	34	8	4365	1715	1150
2.0 DOHC	1996	150	P	S4	F	130	8.5	34	-	4365	1715	1150
LHS												
3.5	3518	257	P	V6	F	130	9.0	-	-	5275	1890	1625
300M												
2.7	2736	203	P	V6	F	124	10.5	-	-	5025	1890	1590
3.5	3518	257	P	V6	F	137	8.0	-	-	5025	1890	1610
Sebring												
2.0	1996	140	P	S4	F	125	10.9	24	-	4760	1770	1335
2.4	2429	150	P	S4	F	124	-	23	-	4902	1780	1520
2.5	2497	155	P	V6	F	131	10.5	20	-	4760	1770	1420
Viper												
8.0	7990	455	P	V10	R	185	4.6	15	20	4448	1924	1590
Voyager												
2.4	2429	150	P	S4	F	120	-	20	-	5070	1950	1600
3.0	2972	150	P	V6	F	120	-	20	-	5070	1950	1708
3.3	3301	158	P	V6	F	120	-	18	-	5070	1950	1752
3.8	3778	166	P	V6	F	120	-	17	-	5070	1950	1792
2.5 TD	2500	115	D	S4	F	104	-	25	-	5070	1950	1850
Jeep Wrangler												
2.5	2464	122	P	S4	4X4	94	13.6	25	12	3860	1690	1405
4.0	3960	184	P	S6	4X4	100	8.8	23	14	3860	1690	1465
Jeep Cherokee												
2.5	2464	122	P	S4	4X4	103	12.1	25	13	4240	1790	1380
4.0	3960	184	P	S6	4X4	112	9.5	20	14	4240	1790	1440
2.5 TD	2499	115	D	S4	4X4	103	13.1	29	13	4240	1790	1470
Jeep Grand Cherokee												
4.0	3964	196	P	S6	4X4	-	-	-	-	4610	1752	1825
4.7	-	230	P	V8	4X4	-	-	-	-	4610	1752	1875
3.1 TD	-	150	D	S5	4X4	-	-	-	-	4610	1752	1760

CITROEN

	Engine cc	Power bhp	Fuel	Engine config.	Driven wheels	Top Speed mph	0-60mph secs	MPG average	Insurance group	Length mm	Width mm	Weight kg
Saxo												
1.0	954	50	P	S4	F	93	19.1	45	-	3720	1595	805
1.1	1124	60	P	S4	F	102	14.5	42	4	3720	1595	805
1.4	1361	75	P	S4	F	109	11.9	41	5	3720	1595	840
1.6 8v	1587	88	P	S4	F	116	11.6	39	6	3720	1595	905
1.6 16v	1587	118	P	S4	F	127	7.2	35	14	3720	1595	935
1.5 D	1527	57	D	S4	F	98	16.8	53	4	3720	1595	910

CITROEN cont'd

	Engine cc	Power bhp	Fuel	Engine config.	Driven wheels	Top Speed mph	0-60mph secs	MPG average	Insurance group	Length mm	Width mm	Weight kg
Xsara												
1.4	1361	75	P	S4	F	109	14.1	39	6	4167	1698	1020
1.6	1587	88	P	S4	F	113	13.1	37	7	4167	1698	1070
1.8 8v	1762	90	P	S4	F	113	13.1	36	-	4167	1698	1100
1.8 8v (auto only)	1762	101	P	S4	F	110	15.4	31	-	4167	1698	1025
1.8 16v	1762	110	P	S4	F	121	10.7	33	10	4167	1698	1110
2.0	1998	163	P	S4	F	137	8.7	30	16	4167	1698	1190
1.9 Diesel	1905	68	D	S4	F	101	17.2	44	6	4167	1698	1090
1.9 Turbo Diesel	1905	90	D	S4	F	111	12.8	43	7	4167	1698	1140
Xantia												
1.6	1580	88	P	S4	F	109	15.2	32	-	4445	1755	1170
1.8 8v	1762	90	P	S4	F	112	14.5	33	12	4445	1755	1245
1.8 16v	1761	112	P	S4	F	120	11.9	33	12	4445	1755	1175
2.0 8v	1998	121	P	S4	F	121	13.6	28	-	4445	1755	1260
2.0 16v	1998	135	P	S4	F	126	9.3	31	13	4445	1755	1240
2.0 Turbo	1998	147	P	S4	F	132	8.9	29	14	4445	1755	1375
3.0	2946	190	P	V6	F	142	8.2	-	-	4445	1755	1210
1.9 TD	1905	71	D	S4	F	99	16.2	41	8	4445	1755	1210
1.9 TD	1905	92	D	S4	F	111	13.9	41	9	4445	1755	1250
2.1 TD	2088	109	D	S4	F	119	12.5	40	11	4445	1755	1385
XM												
2.0	1998	135	P	S4	F	127	9.1	29	14	4710	1795	1395
2.0 Turbo	1998	150	P	S4	F	133	8.2	27	15	4710	1795	1415
2.1 TD	2088	110	D	S4	F	119	11.0	40	14	4710	1795	1440
2.4 TD	2445	130	D	S4	F	124	10.4	37	14	4710	1795	1585
3.0 V6	2946	190	P	V6	F	136	9.2	22	16	4710	1795	1550
Berlingo Multispace												
1.8	1761	90	P	S4	F	100	12.2	32	5	4108	1719	1170
Synergie												
1.8	1762	99	P	S4	F	103	16.2	28	-	4455	1820	1455
2.0	1998	123	P	S4	F	111	14.6	27	10	4455	1820	1510
2.0 Turbo	1998	150	P	S4	F	122	11.0	27	-	4455	1820	1575
1.9 TD	1905	92	D	S4	F	100	17.2	35	10	4455	1820	1565
2.1 TD	2088	109	D	S4	F	108	14.1	34	-	4455	1820	1515

DACIA

	Engine cc	Power bhp	Fuel	Engine config.	Driven wheels	Top Speed mph	0-60mph secs	MPG average	Insurance group	Length mm	Width mm	Weight kg
1310												
1.4	1397	63	P	S4	F	88	-	35	-	4150	1610	940
1.6	1557	72	P	S4	F	93	-	33	-	4150	1610	940
1.6 D	1588	69	D	S4	F	100	19.0	44	-	4150	1610	940

DAEWOO

	Engine cc	Power bhp	Fuel	Engine config.	Driven wheels	Top Speed mph	0-60mph secs	MPG average	Insurance group	Length mm	Width mm	Weight kg
Matiz												
0.8	796	56	P	S3	F	89	-	49	-	3500	1495	750
Lanos												
1.4	1349	74	P	S4	F	104	14.8	36	4	4074	1678	1005
1.6	1598	107	P	S4	F	113	11.3	34	6	4074	1678	1005
Nubira												
1.6	1598	107	P	S4	F	116	10.8	32	7	4467	1700	1153
2.0	1998	136	P	S4	F	122	8.8	31	11	4467	1700	1153
Leganza												
2.0 8v	1998	116	P	S4	F	116	12.2	-	-	4671	1779	1220
2.0 16v	1998	136	P	S4	F	128	10.2	31	11	4671	1779	1250

DAIHATSU

	Engine cc	Power bhp	Fuel	Engine config.	Driven wheels	Top Speed mph	0-60mph secs	MPG average	Insurance group	Length mm	Width mm	Weight kg
Move	847	42	P	S3	F	82	17.6	47	2	3310	1395	745
Cuore	847	42	P	S3	F	85	15.6	53	4	3310	1440	700
Sirion	989	56	P	S3	F	84	15.2	51	5	3675	1595	810
Charade												
1.0	993	52	P	S3	F	87	-	-	-	4100	1620	830
1.3	1296	82	P	S4	F	105	11.2	42	8	4100	1620	820
1.5	1499	88	P	S4	F	105	10.8	40	10	4100	1620	840
1.6	1590	105	P	S4	F	115	9.6	-	-	4100	1620	875
Grand Move												
1.5	1499	90	P	S4	F	103	12.3	37	8	4050	1640	990
Terios												
1.3	1296	82	P	S4	4x4	91	16.1	33	7	3845	1555	1040
Fourtrak												
2.8 TD	2765	101	D	S4	4x4	84	-	30	8	4165	4165	1600

FERRARI

	Engine cc	Power bhp	Fuel	Engine config.	Driven wheels	Top Speed mph	0-60mph secs	MPG average	Insurance group	Length mm	Width mm	Weight kg
F355	3496	375	P	V8	R	175	4.5	17	20	4250	1900	1350
550M	5474	485	P	V12	R	199	4.4	12	20	4550	1935	1640
456M GT	5474	436	P	V12	R	192	5.2	13	20	4730	1920	1690

FIAT

	Engine cc	Power bhp	Fuel	Engine config.	Driven wheels	Top Speed mph	0-60mph secs	MPG average	Insurance group	Length mm	Width mm	Weight kg
Seicento												
0.9	899	40	P	S4	F	87	18	46	1	3332	1508	720
1.1	1108	55	P	S4	F	93	14	46	3	3332	1508	750
Palio												
1.0	994	61	P	S4	F	94	16.3	43	-	3740	1610	890
1.2	1241	73	P	S4	F	103	13.2	39	-	3740	1610	1025
1.5	1497	76	P	S4	F	102	12.8	42	-	3740	1610	925
1.6	1581	106	P	S4	F	116	9.5	34	-	3740	1610	960
1.7 TD	1698	69	D	S4	F	102	14.9	49	-	3740	1610	1110
Punto												
1.1	1108	54	P	S4	F	93	16.5	44	-	3760	1625	840
1.2	1242	60	P	S4	F	99	14.9	42	3	3760	1625	865
1.2	1242	75	P	S4	F	106	12.0	40	5	3760	1625	875
1.4 GT	1372	136	P	S4	F	124	7.9	34	14	3760	1625	1000
1.7 TD 60	1698	63	D	S4	F	96	16.8	44	4	3760	1625	1010
1.7 TD 70	1698	69	D	S4	F	101	14.8	44	5	3760	1625	1010
Brava												
1.4	1370	80	P	S4	F	106	13.8	36	5	4025	1755	1040
1.6	1581	103	P	S4	F	112	11.5	34	7	4025	1755	1090
1.8	1747	113	P	S4	F	120	10.0	34	9	4025	1755	1130
1.9 D	1929	65	D	S4	F	97	17.8	43	-	4025	1755	1100
1.9 TD 75	1910	75	D	S4	F	102	15.5	45	6	4025	1755	1170
1.9 TD 100	1910	100	D	S4	F	112	11.0	44	8	4025	1755	1180
Bravo												
1.4	1370	80	P	S4	F	106	13.8	36	5	4185	1755	1040
1.6	1581	103	P	S4	F	112	11.5	34	7	4185	1755	1090
1.8	1747	113	P	S4	F	120	10.0	34	6	4185	1755	1130
2.0	1996	147	P	S5	F	131	8.5	29	14	4380	1740	1190
1.9 Diesel	1929	65	D	S4	F	97	17.8	43	-	4185	1755	1130
1.9 TD	1910	75	D	S4	F	102	15.5	45	6	4185	1755	1145
1.9 TD	1910	100	D	S4	F	112	11.0	44	8	4185	1755	1155
Marea												
1.4	1370	80	P	S4	F	106	13.8	36	10	4380	1740	1085
1.6	1581	103	P	S4	F	112	11.5	34	11	4380	1740	1140
1.8	1747	113	P	S4	F	120	10.0	34	-	4380	1740	1195
2.0	1996	147	P	S5	F	131	8.5	29	14	4380	1740	1255
1.9 TD 75	1910	75	D	S4	F	102	15.5	45	8	4380	1740	1185
1.9 TD 100	1910	100	D	S4	F	112	11.0	44	10	4380	1740	1190
2.4 TD	2387	124	D	S5	F	121	10.5	37	12	4380	1740	1280
barchetta												
1.8	1747	130	P	S4	F	125	8.9	33	16	3915	1640	1060
Coupe												
1.8	1747	130	P	S4	F	127	9.2	33	-	4250	1765	1180
2.0	1998	147	P	S5	F	132	8.9	29	17	4250	1765	1270
2.0 Turbo	1998	220	P	S5	F	155	6.5	28	19	4250	1765	1310
Ulysse												
1.8	1762	99	P	S4	F	110	14.3	29	-	4455	1820	1575
2.0	1998	123	P	S4	F	111	13.1	27	10	4455	1820	1510
2.0 Turbo	1998	150	P	S4	F	122	11.0	22	-	4455	1820	1575
1.9 TD	1905	92	D	S4	F	100	17.2	35	10	4455	1820	1565
2.1 TD	2088	109	D	S4	F	109	13.3	-	-	4455	1820	1615

FORD

	Engine cc	Power bhp	Fuel	Engine config.	Driven wheels	Top Speed mph	0-60mph secs	MPG average	Insurance group	Length mm	Width mm	Weight kg
Ka												
1.3	1299	60	P	S4	F	96	13.8	48	2	3620	1631	871
Fiesta												
1.3	1299	50	P	S4	F	89	19.5	41	-	3745	1605	949
1.3	1299	60	P	S4	F	96	14.8	42	4	3745	1605	949
1.25 16v	1242	75	P	S4	F	106	11.9	42	5	3745	1605	940
1.4 16v	1388	90	P	S4	F	112	10.8	39	7	3745	1605	940
1.8 Diesel	1753	60	D	S4	F	96	16.2	48	5	3745	1605	1022
Escort												
1.3	1299	60	P	S4	F	95	16.4	42	4	4290	1690	990
1.4	1392	71	P	S4	F	101	14.4	39	5	4290	1690	1030
1.6	1598	90	P	S4	F	110	12.2	36	6	4290	1690	1065
1.8 GTi	1753	116	P	S4	F	122	9.2	38	13	4290	1690	1065
1.8 Diesel	1753	60	D	S4	F	95	16.7	44	6	4290	1690	1080
1.8 TD	1753	90	D	S4	F	106	10.8	58	7	4290	1690	1115
Focus												
1.4	1398	75	P	S4	F	106	14.1	44	-	4152	1699	1068
1.6	1596	100	P	S4	F	115	10.9	41	-	4152	1699	1070
1.8	1796	115	P	S4	F	123	10.2	37	-	4152	1699	1125
2.0	1989	130	P	S4	F	125	9.2	33	-	4152	1699	1146
1.8 TD	1753	90	D	S4	F	114	12.4	58	-	4152	1699	1183
Mondeo												
1.6i	1598	90	P	S4	F	112	12.9	37	7	4480	1745	1220

FORD cont'd

	Engine cc	Power bhp	Fuel	Engine config.	Driven wheels	Top Speed mph	0-60mph secs	MPG average	Insurance group	Length mm	Width mm	Weight kg
1.8i	1796	115	P	S4	F	121	10.2	34	9	4480	1745	1220
2.0i	1989	130	P	S4	F	128	9.4	34	11	4480	1745	1240
2.5i	2544	170	P	V6	F	139	8.0	29	15	4480	1745	1315
1.8 TD	1753	90	D	S4	F	112	12.3	44	8	4480	1745	1285
Puma												
1.4	1388	90	P	S4	F	112	10.8	38	9	3894	1674	1035
1.7	1679	125	P	S4	F	126	8.8	38	12	3894	1674	1040
Cougar												
2.0	1988	131	P	S4	F	130	10.0	35	-	4700	1770	1300
2.5	2544	170	P	V6	F	140	8.5	30	-	4700	1770	1375
Galaxy												
2.0	1998	115	P	S4	F	110	12.0	28	11	4615	1810	1560
2.3	2995	145	P	S4	F	119	10.7	28	12	4615	1810	1565
2.8	2792	174	P	V6	F	124	10.0	21	14	4615	1810	1670
1.9 TD	1896	90	D	S4	F	100	15.4	43	11	4615	1810	1670
1.9 TD 110	1896	110	D	S4	F	107	16.4	43	11	4615	1810	1670
Explorer												
4.0	3996	162	P	V6	4x4	105	12.7	17	16	4530	1790	1670
4.9	4942	213	P	V8	4x4	115	10.6	14	-	4530	1790	1670

FORD US

	Engine cc	Power bhp	Fuel	Engine config.	Driven wheels	Top Speed mph	0-60mph secs	MPG average	Insurance group	Length mm	Width mm	Weight kg
Contour												
2.0	1988	125	P	S4	F	122	10.6	22	-	4670	1755	1256
2.5	2544	170	P	V6	F	140	8.6	20	-	4670	1755	1355
Taurus												
3.0	2986	145	P	V6	F	112	-	20	-	5015	1855	1510
3.0-24V	2967	200	P	V6	F	131	-	19	-	5015	1855	1515
Mustang												
3.8	3797	150	P	V6	R	112	9.3	20	-	4610	1825	1390
4.6	4601	215	P	V8	R	134	-	17	-	4610	1825	1390
4.6 DOHC	4601	305	P	V8	R	150	5.5	18	-	4610	1825	1390
Windstar												
3.0	2979	152	P	V6	F	112	13.5	-	-	5125	1915	1710
3.8	3797	203	P	V6	F	109	-	-	-	5125	1915	1690

FORD Australia

	Engine cc	Power bhp	Fuel	Engine config.	Driven wheels	Top Speed mph	0-60mph secs	MPG average	Insurance group	Length mm	Width mm	Weight kg
Festiva												
1.3	1323	63	P	S4	F	-	-	47	-	3915	1670	912
1.5	1498	75	P	S4	F	-	-	47	-	3915	1670	936
Laser												
1.6	1598	107	P	S4	F	-	-	40	-	4215	1710	1098
1.8	1840	123	P	S4	F	-	-	37	-	4215	1710	1088
Falcon												
4.0	3987	213	P	S6	R	130	8.0	23	-	4900	1860	1535
4.9	4942	224	P	V8	R	137	-	23	-	4900	1860	1535
4.9 GT	4942	272	P	V8	R	143	7.1	20	-	4900	1860	1645

FSO

	Engine cc	Power bhp	Fuel	Engine config.	Driven wheels	Top Speed mph	0-60mph secs	MPG average	Insurance group	Length mm	Width mm	Weight kg
Caro												
1.5	1481	75	P	S4	R	92	18.8	35	-	4320	1650	1190
1.9 D	1905	69	D	S4	R	87	21.8	42	-	4320	1650	1210

HINDUSTAN

	Engine cc	Power bhp	Fuel	Engine config.	Driven wheels	Top Speed mph	0-60mph secs	MPG average	Insurance group	Length mm	Width mm	Weight kg
Ambassador												
1.8	1817	88	P	S4	R	88	20.0	26	-	4310	1675	1105

HOLDEN

	Engine cc	Power bhp	Fuel	Engine config.	Driven wheels	Top Speed mph	0-60mph secs	MPG average	Insurance group	Length mm	Width mm	Weight kg
Commodore												
3.8	3791	200	P	V6	R	125	8.7	19	-	4860	1795	1360
5.0	4987	225	P	V8	R	131	8.3	17	-	4860	1795	1420
5.0 SS	4987	252	P	V8	R	144	8.0	17	-	4860	1795	1420
5.7 HSV	5733	292	P	V8	R	156	6.5	15	-	4860	1795	1600

HONDA

	Engine cc	Power bhp	Fuel	Engine config.	Driven wheels	Top Speed mph	0-60mph secs	MPG average	Insurance group	Length mm	Width mm	Weight kg
Logo												
1.3	1343	67	P	S4	F	99	-	42	-	3750	1645	790
Civic												
1.4	1396	75	P	S4	F	103	13.9	42	7	4460	1695	1030
1.4	1396	89	P	S4	F	111	13.1	45	9	4460	1695	1075
1.5	1493	112	P	S4	F	109	12.2	43	9	4460	1695	1080
1.6	1590	111	P	S4	F	119	10.2	37	11	4460	1695	1125
1.6 SR	1590	124	P	S4	F	122	9.9	40	13	4460	1695	1125
1.6 Type R	1595	185	P	S4	F	112	5.7	-	-	4460	1695	1125
1.8 VTi	1797	169	P	S4	F	139	8.3	32	15	4460	1695	1225
2.0 TD	1994	86	D	S4	F	106	14.4	50	8	4460	1695	1225

HONDA cont'd

	Engine cc	Power bhp	Fuel	Engine config.	Driven wheels	Top Speed mph	0-60mph secs	MPG average	Insurance group	Length mm	Width mm	Weight kg
Accord												
1.8	1850	136	P	S4	F	127	10.4	34	10	4595	1750	1405
2.0	1997	147	P	S4	F	130	9.9	32.8	11	4595	1750	1405
2.2 Type R	2157	212	P	S4	F	142	7.2	29.4	-	4595	1750	1405
3.0 Auto	2997	200	P	V6	F	140	8.5	26.4	-	4595	1750	1450
Legend												
3.5	3474	205	P	V6	F	134	9.1	23	17	4980	1810	1675
Integra												
1.8	1834	144	P	S4	F	124	-	33	-	4525	1710	1145
1.8	1797	173	P	S4	F	134	-	32	-	4525	1710	1200
1.8 Type-R	1797	190	P	S4	F	145	6.7	32	18	4380	1695	1120
Prelude												
2.0	1997	134	P	S4	F	126	9.2	31	15	4545	1750	1240
2.2	2157	185	P	S4	F	143	7.5	30	17	4545	1750	1319
NSX												
3.0	2977	252	P	V6	R	160	6.5	27	20	4430	1810	1370
3.2	3179	290	P	V6	R	170	5.5	24	20	4430	1810	1370
Shuttle												
2.2 auto	2156	150	P	S4	F	114	12.2	27	16	4750	1770	1470
CR-V												
2.0	1973	131	P	S4	4X4	103	12.5	28	10	4470	1750	1340

HYUNDAI

	Engine cc	Power bhp	Fuel	Engine config.	Driven wheels	Top Speed mph	0-60mph secs	MPG average	Insurance group	Length mm	Width mm	Weight kg
Atoz												
1.0	999	54	P	S4	F	93	15.1	45	2	3495	1495	800
Accent												
1.3	1341	84	P	S4	F	108	12.6	38	6	4115	1620	935
1.5 12V	1495	88	P	S4	F	109	11.4	33	8	4115	1620	965
1.5 16v	1495	99	P	S4	F	112	10.5	32	7	4115	1620	970
Lantra												
1.6	1599	116	P	S4	F	120	11.2	37	8	4460	1702	1185
2.0	1975	138	P	S4	F	126	9.2	34	11	4460	1702	1226
Sonata												
2.0	1997	136	P	S4	F	124	9.6	32	13	4710	1818	1330
2.5	2493	160	P	S4	F	124	9.3	28	14	4710	1818	1385
Coupe												
1.6	1600	114	P	S4	F	120	9.8	34	9	4340	1730	1235
1.8	1796	132	P	S4	F	118	-	32	-	4340	1730	1165
2.0	1975	137	P	S4	F	123	10.7	25	12	4340	1730	1250

ISUZU

	Engine cc	Power bhp	Fuel	Engine config.	Driven wheels	Top Speed mph	0-60mph secs	MPG average	Insurance group	Length mm	Width mm	Weight kg
Vehi-Cross												
3.2	3165	215	P	V6	4x4	106	-	-	-	4130	1790	1750
Trooper												
3.5	3494	212	P	V6	4x4	112	11.3	20.6	-	4760	1835	1890
3.0 D	2999	157	D	S4	4x4	99	15.8	25.9	-	4760	1835	1990

JAGUAR

	Engine cc	Power bhp	Fuel	Engine config.	Driven wheels	Top Speed mph	0-60mph secs	MPG average	Insurance group	Length mm	Width mm	Weight kg
XJ8												
3.2	3253	237	P	V8	R	140	8.1	24	16	5149	1799	1710
4.0	3996	284	P	V8	R	149	6.9	24	17	5149	1799	1710
4.0 S'charged XJR	3996	363	P	V8	R	155	5.3	22	19	5149	1799	1775
XK8												
4.0	3996	290	P	V8	R	155	6.4	23	19	4760	1830	1705
4.0 S'charged XKR	3996	363	P	V8	R	155	5.3	22	19	4760	1830	1650

KIA

	Engine cc	Power bhp	Fuel	Engine config.	Driven wheels	Top Speed mph	0-60mph secs	MPG average	Insurance group	Length mm	Width mm	Weight kg
Pride												
1.3	1324	64	P	S4	F	100	11.8	43	5	3475	1605	750
Mentor												
1.5	1498	80	P	S4	F	106	12.8	36	6	4360	1690	1055
1.6	1598	106	P	S4	F	111	11.8	35	-	4360	1690	1055
1.8	1840	124	P	S4	F	119	10.3	34	-	4360	1690	1115
Credos												
1.8	1793	116	P	S4	F	115	10.7	-	-	4695	1770	1220
2.0	1998	133	P	S4	F	121	10.9	-	-	4695	1770	1235
Sportage												
2.0	1998	95	P	S4	R	99	18.4	24	-	4245	1730	1420
2.0 16v	1998	128	P	S4	R	107	14.7	24	9	4245	1730	1420
2.2 D	2184	63	D	S4	R	81	-	28	-	4245	1730	1465
2.0 TD	1998	83	D	S4	R	90	20.4	32	-	4245	1730	1465

LADA

Samara
1.1	1099	53	P	S4	F	85	14.1	39	-	4005	1620	900
1.3	1288	65	P	S4	F	92	14.5	38	-	4005	1620	915
1.5	1499	75	P	S4	F	100	12.0	38	-	4005	1620	930

Niva
| 1.6 | 1568 | 78 | P | S4 | 4X4 | 82 | 22.0 | 27 | - | 3720 | 1676 | 1150 |
| 1.9 D | 1905 | 64 | D | S4 | 4X4 | 78 | 25.0 | 38 | - | 3720 | 1676 | 1180 |

110
1.5	1500	79	P	S4	F	103	12.5	-	-	4285	1675	1000
1.5 16v	1500	94	P	S4	F	109	11.5	-	-	4285	1675	1000
2.0	1998	150	P	S4	F	134	8.5	-	-	4310	1750	1100

LAMBORGHINI

Diablo
| 5.7 | 5707 | 492 | P | V12 | R | 202 | 4.1 | 14 | 20 | 4460 | 2040 | 1575 |
| 5.7 SV | 5707 | 500 | P | V12 | R | 186 | 3.9 | 14 | 20 | 4470 | 2040 | 1530 |

LANCIA

Y
1.1	1108	54	P	S4	F	93	15.0	45	-	3735	1690	850
1.2	1242	60	P	S4	F	100	13.3	45	-	3735	1690	860
1.4	1371	80	P	S4	F	106	12.4	43	-	3735	1690	920

Delta
1.6	1581	103	P	S4	F	118	11	34	-	4010	1705	1130
1.8	1747	113	P	S4	F	121	10.3	32	-	4010	1705	1170
1.8	1747	131	P	S4	F	124	9.4	32	-	4010	1705	1200
2.0 Turbo	1995	186	P	S4	F	138	7.5	27	-	4010	1705	1330
1.9 TD	1929	90	D	S4	F	113	12.0	42	-	4010	1705	1280

Dedra
1.6	1581	90	P	S4	F	113	13.4	33	-	4345	1700	1180
1.8	1747	131	P	S4	F	126	10.0	32	-	4345	1700	1255
1.9 TD	1929	90	D	S4	F	113	12.9	42	-	4345	1700	1225

Kappa
2.0	1998	145	P	S5	F	128	9.8	29	-	4685	1825	1440
2.0 Turbo	1995	205	P	S4	F	147	7.3	26	-	4685	1825	1480
2.4	2446	175	P	S5	F	134	9.2	26	-	4685	1825	1450
3.0	2959	204	P	V6	F	141	8.0	27	-	4685	1825	1510
2.4 TD	2387	124	D	S5	F	121	11.5	34	-	4685	1825	1485

LAND ROVER

Freelander
| 1.8 | 1795 | 120 | P | S4 | 4X4 | 103 | 11.9 | 28 | 8 | 4382 | 1805 | 1380 |
| 2.0 TD | 1994 | 98 | D | S4 | 4X4 | 96 | 15.2 | 37 | 8 | 4382 | 1805 | 1405 |

Defender
3.9	3947	182	P	V8	4X4	87	-	18	-	3720	1790	1630
2.5 TDi 90	2495	111	D	S4	4X4	85	15.1	28	7	3720	1790	1695
2.5 TDi 110	2495	111	D	S4	4X4	80	17.4	29	7	4440	1790	1870

Discovery
Details unavailable at time of going to press

Range Rover
4.0	3947	190	P	V8	4X4	118	9.9	25	14	4715	1850	2090
4.6	4554	225	P	V8	4X4	125	9.3	23	15	4715	1850	2150
2.5 TD	2497	134	D	S6	4X4	105	13.3	32	13	4715	1850	2115

LEXUS
IS200	-	-	P	S6	R	-	-	-	-	4400	1720	-
GS300	2997	209	P	S6	R	143	8.6	33	17	4965	1795	1720
LS400	3969	260	P	V8	R	156	7.4	29	19	4995	1830	1680

LINCOLN
Continental	4601	260	P	V8	F	134	-	26	-	5240	1870	1765
Town Car	4601	213	P	V8	R	112	-	26	-	5560	1950	1835
Navigator	5403	232	P	V8	4X4	118	-	18	-	5200	2030	2335

LS6/8
Details unavailable at time of going to press

LOTUS
| Elise | 1795 | 116 | P | S4 | R | 126 | 5.9 | 40 | 17 | 3726 | 1701 | 690 |

Esprit
| 2.0 | 1994 | 240 | P | S4 | R | 163 | 5.2 | 23 | 20 | 4414 | 1883 | 1300 |
| 3.5 | 3506 | 349 | P | V8 | R | 175 | 4.5 | 21 | 20 | 4414 | 1883 | 1380 |

MAHINDRA
2.1	2112	63	D	S4	4X4	65	-	28	-	3810	1800	1300
2.5	2523	55	D	S4	4X4	65	-	30	-	3810	1800	1300
2.5	2498	72	D	S4	4X4	70	-	28	-	4340	1800	1600

MARCOS

MantaRay
2.0	1994	135	P	S4	R	124	5.6	-	-	4005	1680	1050
2.0 turbo	1994	200	P	S4	R	137	5.1	-	-	4005	1680	1050
4.0	3946	190	P	V8	R	169	4.6	-	20	4005	1680	1075

LM500
LM 4.0	3950	190	P	V8	R	143	5.4	-	20	4263	1828	1120
LM 5.0	4998	320	P	V8	R	168	4.6	-	20	4263	1828	1120
Mantis	4600	352	P	V8	R	170	4.1	26	20	4263	1828	1078

MASERATI

Coupe
Details unavailable at time of going to press

Quattroporte
2.0 twin-turbo	1996	287	P	V6	R	163	5.9	31	20	4550	1810	1545
2.8 twin-turbo	2790	284	P	V6	R	159	5.9	28	20	4550	1810	1560
3.2 twin-turbo	3217	335	P	V8	R	169	5.8	21	20	4550	1810	1650

MAZDA

121
1.3	1299	60	P	S4	F	96	14.8	51	4	3745	1605	949
1.25	1242	75	P	S4	F	106	11.9	46	6	3745	1605	940
1.8 D	1753	60	D	S4	F	96	16.2	55	5	3745	1605	1022

Demio
| 1.3 | 1324 | 83 | P | S4 | F | 106 | 13.2 | 40 | 5 | 3808 | 1670 | 910 |
| 1.5 | 1498 | 99 | P | S4 | F | 112 | - | 38 | - | 3808 | 1670 | 970 |

323
| 1.5 | 1498 | 90 | P | S4 | F | 110 | 11.9 | 38 | - | 4200 | 1705 | - |
| 1.8 | 1840 | 115 | P | S4 | F | 121 | 9.8 | 34 | - | 4200 | 1705 | - |

626
1.8	1840	90	P	S4	F	112	12.7	37	8	4575	1710	1216
2.0	1991	115	P	S4	F	124	9.9	36	10	4575	1710	1233
2.0	1991	136	P	S4	F	130	9.6	35	10	4575	1710	1290
2.0 TD	1998	100	D	S4	F	116	11.5	54	10	4575	1710	-

Xedos 6
| 1.6 | 1598 | 107 | P | S4 | F | 110 | 10.3 | 47 | 14 | 4560 | 1695 | 1160 |
| 2.0 | 1995 | 144 | P | V6 | F | 134 | 9.3 | 41 | 16 | 4560 | 1695 | 1200 |

Xedos 9
2.0	1995	143	P	V6	F	126	10.7	42	-	4825	1770	1415
2.5	2497	168	P	V6	F	130	11.0	38	15	4825	1770	1415
2.3	2255	211	P	V6	F	143	9.4	41	-	4825	1770	1500

MX-5
| 1.6 | 1598 | 110 | P | S4 | R | 119 | 9.7 | 35 | 11 | 3975 | 1680 | 1025 |
| 1.8 | 1840 | 140 | P | S4 | R | 127 | 8.0 | 33 | 12 | 3975 | 1680 | 1025 |

MCC
| Smart | 599 | 54 | P | S3 | R | 80 | - | 70 | - | 2500 | 1450 | 650 |

MERCEDES-BENZ

A-Class
A140	1397	82	P	S4	F	106	12.9	40	5	3580	1720	1010
A160	1598	102	P	S4	F	113	10.8	39	6	3580	1720	1030
A160 TD	1689	60	D	S4	F	95	17.7	63	-	3580	1720	1060
A170 TD	1689	90	D	S4	F	109	12.5	57	6	3580	1720	1080

C-Class
C180	1799	122	P	S4	R	120	12.1	30	11	4485	1720	1280
C200	1998	136	P	S4	R	123	11.1	30	12	4485	1720	1295
C230	2295	180	P	S4	R	131	10.6	30	13	4485	1720	1340
C230 K S'charged	2250	193	P	S4	R	144	8.4	29	13	4485	1720	1340
C240	2398	170	P	V6	R	135	9.3	39	13	4485	1720	1345
C280	2799	197	P	V6	R	144	8.3	29	15	4485	1720	1355
C43 AMG	4266	306	P	V8	R	155	6.5	-	-	4485	1720	1495
C220 D	2155	95	D	S4	R	109	16.3	38	11	4485	1720	1310
C220 TD	2151	125	D	S4	R	123	10.5	-	-	4485	1720	1340
C250 TD	2497	150	D	S4	R	127	10.2	34	13	4485	1720	1405

E-Class
E200	1998	136	P	S4	R	128	11.3	29	13	4800	1800	1440
E240	2398	170	P	V6	R	139	9.6	27	14	4800	1800	1375
E280	2799	204	P	V6	R	144	8.5	28	15	4800	1800	1465
E320	3199	224	P	V6	R	148	7.7	24	16	4800	1800	1505
E430	4266	279	P	V8	R	155	6.6	25	17	4800	1800	1575
E55 AMG	5439	354	P	V8	R	155	6.3	24	-	4800	1800	1635
E220 D	2155	95	D	S4	R	113	17.0	37	13	4800	1800	1385
E300 TD	2874	129	D	S5	R	122	11.5	37	-	4800	1800	1465
E320 TD	2996	177	D	S6	R	137	8.9	-	-	4800	1800	1555

S-Class
Details unavailable at time of going to press

MERCEDES–BENZ cont'd

	Engine cc	Power bhp	Fuel	Engine config.	Driven wheels	Top Speed mph	0-60mph secs	MPG average	Insurance group	Length mm	Width mm	Weight kg
CL-Coupe												
CL420	4196	279	P	V8	R	155	8.5	19	18	5065	1895	2005
CL500	4973	320	P	V8	R	155	7.5	18	20	5065	1895	2005
CL600	5987	394	P	V12	R	155	6.6	17	20	5065	1895	2165
CLK												
2.0	1998	136	P	S4	R	129	11.0	29	13	4570	1720	1300
2.0 S'charged	1998	192	P	S4	R	145	8.4	29	-	4570	1720	1320
2.3 S'charged	2295	193	P	S4	R	145	8.4	29	15	4570	1720	1320
3.2	3199	224	P	V6	R	149	7.4	29	16	4570	1720	1300
SLK												
200	1998	136	P	S4	R	129	9.5	30	-	3995	1715	1195
200 K S'charged	1998	192	P	S4	R	144	7.7	30	-	3995	1715	1250
230 K S'charged	2295	193	P	S4	R	142	7.4	30	17	3995	1715	1250
SL												
SL280	2799	193	P	S6	R	140	9.5	23	20	4470	1810	1760
SL320	3199	231	P	S6	R	149	8.1	23	20	4470	1810	1780
SL500	4973	320	P	V8	R	155	6.2	20	20	4470	1810	1800
SL600	5987	389	P	V12	R	155	6.1	20	20	4470	1810	1980
60 AMG	5956	381	P	V8	R	155	5.6	17	-	4470	1810	1855
M-Class												
ML230	2295	150	P	S4	4X4	112	12.3	24	-	4587	1839	1785
ML320	3199	215	P	V6	4X4	112	9.0	22	-	4587	1839	1930
ML430	4266	271	P	V8	4X4	125	7.9	21	-	4587	1839	2000
V-Class												
V230	2295	150	P	S4	F	109	14.5	24	15	4659	1880	-

MERCURY

	Engine cc	Power bhp	Fuel	Engine config.	Driven wheels	Top Speed mph	0-60mph secs	MPG average	Insurance group	Length mm	Width mm	Weight kg
Grand Marquis												
4.6	4601	203	P	V8	R	118	-	26	-	5380	1980	1720

MITSUBISHI

	Engine cc	Power bhp	Fuel	Engine config.	Driven wheels	Top Speed mph	0-60mph secs	MPG average	Insurance group	Length mm	Width mm	Weight kg
Colt												
1.3	1299	75	P	S4	F	106	12.5	36	5	4290	1690	940
1.5	1468	110	P	S4	F	112	10.5	35	-	4290	1690	945
1.6	1597	90	P	S4	F	116	10.5	33	6	4290	1690	975
1.6	1597	175	P	S4	F	130	7.5	-	-	4290	1690	1020
1.8	1829	135	P	V6	F	118	-	30	-	4290	1690	1120
1.8 Turbo	1834	205	P	S4	F	137	7.0	26	-	4290	1690	1240
2.0 Turbo (Lancer)	1997	280	P	S4	4X4	-	-	-	-	4290	1690	1240
2.0 TD	1998	88	D	S4	F	99	16.6	40	-	4290	1690	1080
Carisma												
1.6	1597	90	P	S4	F	113	12.0	38	7	4435	1695	1105
1.8	1834	140	P	S4	F	134	9.2	-	-	4435	1695	1175
1.8 GDi	1834	120	P	S4	F	127	9.4	47	10	4435	1695	1215
1.9 TD	1870	90	D	S4	F	112	13.2	47	8	4435	1695	1155
Galant												
1.8	1834	150	P	S4	F	134	9.0	40	-	4630	1740	1240
2.0	1997	136	P	S4	F	130	9.7	34	12	4630	1740	1260
2.0	1999	145	P	V6	F	125	10.0	32	-	4630	1740	1320
2.4	2351	143	P	S4	F	125	-	28	-	4630	1740	1250
2.5	2498	163	P	V6	F	140	8.5	30	14	4630	1740	1290
2.5 Turbo	2498	280	P		4X4	140	-	25	-	4630	1740	1480
2.0 TD	1998	90	D	S4	F	112	-	42	-	4630	1740	1300
FTO												
1.8	1834	125	P	S4	F	125	-	26	-	4320	1735	1100
2.0	1998	170	P	V6	F	138	-	22	-	4320	1735	1150
2.0	1998	200	P	V6	F	144	-	22	-	4320	1735	1150
3000 GT	2972	281	P	V6	4X4	155	5.7	23	20	4570	1840	1710
Space Star												
Space Runner	} Details unavailable at time of going to press											
Space Wagon												
Space Gear												
2.0	1997	115	P	S4	R	103	-	28	-	5085	1695	1560
2.4	2351	132	P	S4	R	103	-	28	-	5085	1695	1660
3.0	2972	185	P	V6	R	106	-	23	-	5085	1695	2030
2.5 TD	2477	99	D	S4	R	93	-	26	-	5085	1695	1650
2.8 TD	2835	125	D	S4	R	94	-	25	-	5085	1695	2020
Shogun												
3.0	2972	178	P	V6	4X4	109	11.1	18	14	4656	1695	1740
3.5	3497	205	P	V6	4X4	116	10.5	16	15	4656	1695	1890
2.5 TD	2477	98	D	S4	4X4	91	18.1	26	13	4656	1695	1550
2.8 TD	2835	123	D	S4	4X4	94	17.3	21	13	4656	1695	1850
Montero												
3.0	2972	185	P	V6	4X4	106	-	23	-	4530	1775	1830
3.5	3497	245	P	V6	4X4	118	-	23	-	4530	1775	1830
2.8 TD	2835	125	D	S4	4X4	96	-	25	-	4530	1775	1810

MORGAN

	Engine cc	Power bhp	Fuel	Engine config.	Driven wheels	Top Speed mph	0-60mph secs	MPG average	Insurance group	Length mm	Width mm	Weight kg
4/4	1796	114	P	S4	R	112	8.0	-	13	3890	1500	870
Plus 4	1994	135	P	S4	R	115	7.5	-	14	3960	1630	920
Plus 8												
3.9	3946	190	P	V8	R	130	5.6	-	15	3999	1700	940
4.6	4552	233	P	V8	R	-	-	-	-	3999	1700	975

NISSAN

	Engine cc	Power bhp	Fuel	Engine config.	Driven wheels	Top Speed mph	0-60mph secs	MPG average	Insurance group	Length mm	Width mm	Weight kg
Micra												
1.0	998	54	P	S4	F	93	16.4	47	3	3700	1590	775
1.3	1275	75	P	S4	F	106	12.0	43	5	3700	1590	810
Almera												
1.4	1392	87	P	S4	F	108	12.6	41	5	4440	1690	1035
1.6	1597	100	P	S4	F	112	11.0	40	6	4440	1690	1070
2.0	1998	143	P	S4	F	131	8.2	35	14	4120	1690	1070
2.0 TD	1974	75	D	S4	F	98	16.8	46	5	4440	1690	1140
Primera												
1.6	1597	100	P	S4	F	112	12.0	41	8	4430	1715	1165
2.0	1998	130	P	S4	F	127	9.6	36	12	4430	1715	1205
2.0 GT	1998	150	P	S4	F	135	8.6	35	14	4430	1715	1250
2.0 TD	1974	90	D	S4	F	108	14.0	42	9	4430	1715	1260
Skyline												
2.0	1998	131	P	S6	R	118	-	-	-	4675	1780	1280
2.5	2499	190	P	S6	R	130	-	-	-	4675	1780	1320
2.5	2499	250	P	S6	R	143	-	-	-	4675	1780	1370
2.6 twin-turbo	2569	280	P	S6	4X4	155	5.4	23	20	4675	1780	1530
QX												
2.0	1995	138	P	V6	F	126	11.3	29	12	4770	1770	1310
2.5	2496	190	P	V6	F	130	-	28	-	4770	1770	1340
3.0	2988	190	P	V6	F	131	9.6	26	14	4770	1770	1360
200 SX												
2.0	1998	160	P	S4	R	131	-	-	-	4520	1730	1140
2.0 Turbo	1998	203	P	S4	R	146	7.5	37	18	4520	1730	1260
Serena												
1.6	1597	97	P	S4	F	93	18.1	29	10	4315	1695	1385
2.0	1998	140	P	S4	F	106	13.0	27	12	4315	1695	1485
2.3 Diesel	2283	75	D	S4	F	84	26.5	30	10	4315	1695	1485
Terrano II												
2.4	2389	124	P	S4	4X4	99	13.7	24	10	4585	1735	1620
2.7 TD	2663	125	D	S4	4X4	97	16.7	27	10	4585	1735	1730
Patrol												
4.5	4169	200	P	S6	4X4	106	-	19	-	4965	1840	2210
2.8 TD	2826	129	D	S6	4X4	93	17.5	25	13	4965	1840	2070
4.2 TD	4169	145	D	S6	4X4	90	-	21	-	4965	1840	2320

OLDSMOBILE

	Engine cc	Power bhp	Fuel	Engine config.	Driven wheels	Top Speed mph	0-60mph secs	MPG average	Insurance group	Length mm	Width mm	Weight kg
Alero												
2.4	2392	152	P	S4	F	112	10.6	31	-	4740	1780	1340
3.4	3350	173	P	V6	F	118	9.2	30	-	4740	1780	1370
Intrigue	3791	199	P	V6	F	124	-	29	-	4970	1870	1565

PERODUA

	Engine cc	Power bhp	Fuel	Engine config.	Driven wheels	Top Speed mph	0-60mph secs	MPG average	Insurance group	Length mm	Width mm	Weight kg
Nippa	847	42	P	S3	F	84	17.6	53	3	3310	1440	700

PEUGEOT

	Engine cc	Power bhp	Fuel	Engine config.	Driven wheels	Top Speed mph	0-60mph secs	MPG average	Insurance group	Length mm	Width mm	Weight kg
106												
1.1	1124	60	P	S4	F	102	14.5	50	4	3720	1595	805
1.4	1361	75	P	S4	F	109	11.9	51	5	3720	1595	840
1.6	1587	88	P	S4	F	116	11.6	48	6	3720	1595	905
1.6	1587	101	P	S4	F	121	9.6	39	11	3720	1595	895
1.6 16v	1587	118	P	S4	F	122	8.7	39	13	3720	1595	935
1.5 D	1527	57	D	S4	F	98	18.5	53	3	3720	1595	875
206												
1.1	1124	60	P	S4	F	98	16.5	46	-	3835	1652	910
1.4	1361	75	P	S4	F	106	14.4	43	-	3835	1652	950
1.6	1587	90	P	S4	F	115	12.5	40	-	3835	1652	1025
1.9 D	1905	70	D	S4	F	100	17.2	50	-	3835	1652	1010
306												
1.4	1360	75	P	S4	F	102	14.9	39	4	4230	1690	1020
1.6	1597	90	P	S4	F	111	12.9	37	5	4230	1690	1060
1.8	1762	102	P	S4	F	109	12.2	35	5	4230	1690	1080
1.8 16v	1762	110	P	S4	F	118	11.5	32	11	4230	1690	1120
2.0	1998	123	P	S4	F	122	9.2	31	12	4230	1690	1140
2.0 GTi-6	1998	155	P	S4	F	133	8.4	30	15	4230	1690	1160
1.9 D	1905	70	D	S4	F	101	16.9	44	4	4230	1690	1080
1.9 TD	1905	92	D	S4	F	112	12.4	43	5	4230	1690	1120

PEUGEOT cont'd

	Engine cc	Power bhp	Fuel	Engine config.	Driven wheels	Top Speed mph	0-60mph secs	MPG average	Insurance group	Length mm	Width mm	Weight kg
406												
1.6	1580	90	P	S4	F	109	15.3	33	-	4560	1765	1240
1.8	1762	112	P	S4	F	120	12.5	32	10	4560	1765	1275
2.0	1998	135	P	S4	F	127	11.0	31	12	4560	1765	1315
2.0 Turbo	1998	150	P	S4	F	130	10.3	29	13	4560	1765	1315
2.9	2946	190	P	V6	F	144	8.2	25	16	4560	1765	1455
1.9 TD	1905	92	D	S4	F	111	14.3	35	9	4560	1765	1335
2.1 TD	2088	110	D	S4	F	119	12.5	35	11	4560	1765	1415
new Diesel												
605												
2.0	1998	133	P	S4	F	127	10.9	25	-	4765	1800	1415
2.0	1998	145	P	S4	F	132	10.0	24	15	4765	1800	1485
2.9	2946	190	P	V6	F	146	8.4	24	-	4765	1800	1540
2.1 TD	2088	110	D	S4	F	119	13.1	40	14	4765	1800	1360
2.4 TD	2446	129	D	S4	F	125	12.1	37	-	4765	1800	1600
806												
2.0	1998	123	P	S4	F	111	14.6	27	10	4455	1820	1510
2.0 Turbo	1998	150	P	S4	F	122	11.0	34	-	4455	1820	1575
1.9 TD	1905	92	D	S4	F	100	17.2	35	10	4455	1820	1565
2.1 TD	2088	109	D	S4	F	109	14.4	37	-	4455	1820	1615

PLYMOUTH

	Engine cc	Power bhp	Fuel	Engine config.	Driven wheels	Top Speed mph	0-60mph secs	MPG average	Insurance group	Length mm	Width mm	Weight kg
Prowler												
3.5	3518	250	P	V6	R	118	6.0	25	-	4190	1930	1350

PONTIAC

	Engine cc	Power bhp	Fuel	Engine config.	Driven wheels	Top Speed mph	0-60mph secs	MPG average	Insurance group	Length mm	Width mm	Weight kg
Grand Am												
2.4	2392	152	P	S4	F	118	9.0	-	-	4730	1790	1385
3.4	3350	173	P	V6	F	118	9.5	-	-	4730	1790	1385
Grand Prix												
3.1	3135	160	P	V6	F	122	-	18	-	4990	1845	1540
3.8	3791	195	P	V6	F	125	-	16	-	4990	1845	1540
3.8 S'charged	3791	245	P	V6	F	141	-	16	-	4990	1845	1540
Firebird												
3.8	3791	203	P	V6	R	124	-	22	-	4970	1890	1485
5.7	5733	288	P	V8	R	155	6.0	21	-	4970	1890	1560

PORSCHE

	Engine cc	Power bhp	Fuel	Engine config.	Driven wheels	Top Speed mph	0-60mph secs	MPG average	Insurance group	Length mm	Width mm	Weight kg
Boxster	2480	204	P	F6	R	149	6.9	39	17	4320	1780	1250
911	3387	300	P	F6	R	174	5.4	28	20	4430	1765	1320

PROTON

	Engine cc	Power bhp	Fuel	Engine config.	Driven wheels	Top Speed mph	0-60mph secs	MPG average	Insurance group	Length mm	Width mm	Weight kg
Compact												
1.3	1299	75	P	S4	F	103	13.6	35	8	3990	1700	930
1.5	1468	89	P	S4	F	108	12.1	34	9	3990	1700	940
1.6	1597	111	P	S4	F	116	10.8	34	11	3990	1700	160
Persona												
1.5	1468	89	P	S4	F	108	12.1	34	9	4360	1690	975
1.6	1597	111	P	S4	F	116	10.8	35	11	4360	1690	1045
1.8	1834	133	P	S4	F	126	9.0	30	13	4360	1690	1100
2.0D	1998	68	D	S4	F	99	18.5	40	11	4360	1690	1115

RENAULT

	Engine cc	Power bhp	Fuel	Engine config.	Driven wheels	Top Speed mph	0-60mph secs	MPG average	Insurance group	Length mm	Width mm	Weight kg
Twingo												
1.1	1149	58	P	S4	F	93	13.4	40	-	3435	1630	815
Clio												
1.1	1149	58	P	S4	F	99	15.0	46	2	3708	1626	880
1.4	1390	75	P	S4	F	106	12.1	42	4	3708	1626	940
1.6	1598	90	P	S4	F	112	10.6	39	7	3708	1626	965
1.6 16v	1598	107	P	S4	F	121	9.6	-	-	3708	1626	995
1.9 D	1870	64	D	S4	F	100	15.4	47	3	3708	1626	975
Megane												
1.4	1390	70	P	S4	F	105	14.3	37	3	4130	1700	1015
1.6 75	1598	75	P	S4	F	109	12.9	37	-	4130	1700	1055
1.6 90	1598	90	P	S4	F	116	11.5	37	5	130	1700	1055
2.0	1998	113	P	S4	F	125	9.7	32	8	130	1700	1085
2.0 16v	1998	150	P	S4	F	134	8.6	31	13	3930	1700	1095
1.9	1870	64	D	S4	F	100	16.5	43	4	4130	1700	1110
1.9 TDi	1870	90	D	S4	F	113	12.3	40	6	4130	1700	1130
Megane Scenic												
1.4	1390	75	P	S4	F	99	16.2	30	-	4130	1720	1215
1.6	1598	75	P	S4	F	101	14.7	30	5	4130	1720	1220
1.6	1598	90	P	S4	F	106	13.7	32	-	4130	1720	1220
2.0	1998	114	P	S4	F	115	12.5	30	8	4130	1720	1270
1.9 TDi	1870	98	D	S4	F	108	12.9	41	6	4130	1720	1300

RENAULT cont'd

	Engine cc	Power bhp	Fuel	Engine config.	Driven wheels	Top Speed mph	0-60mph secs	MPG average	Insurance group	Length mm	Width mm	Weight kg
Laguna												
1.6	1598	100	P	S4	F	121	11.5	38	9	4508	1752	1250
2.0	1998	114	P	S4	F	124	10.6	32	10	4508	1752	1245
2.0 16v	1948	139	P	S4	F	130	9.8	32	13	4508	1752	1285
3.0	2946	190	P	V6	F	146	7.7	26	15	4508	1752	1375
2.2 D	2188	83	D	S4	F	109	15.3	40	9	4508	1752	1335
2.2 TD	2188	113	D	S4	F	121	11.8	32	12	4508	1752	1405
Safrane												
2.0	1948	138	P	S4	F	124	12.6	31	14	4750	1820	1370
2.5	2435	168	P	S5	F	133	9.1	26	15	4750	1820	1400
3.0 V6	2963	167	P	V6	F	130	10.2	19	-	4750	1820	1600
2.2 TD	2188	115	D	S4	F	115	12.6	34	-	4750	1820	1410
Espace												
2.0	1998	114	P	S4	F	109	13.7	26	11	4520	1810	1490
3.0 V6	2963	167	P	V6	F	121	11.0	21	14	4520	1810	1650
2.2 TD	2188	113	D	S4	F	109	14.5	35	11	4520	1810	1630
Sport Spider												
2.0	1998	150	P	S4	R	131	6.5	34	18	3795	1830	790

ROLLS-ROYCE

	Engine cc	Power bhp	Fuel	Engine config.	Driven wheels	Top Speed mph	0-60mph secs	MPG average	Insurance group	Length mm	Width mm	Weight kg
Silver Seraph												
5.4	5379	326	P	V12	R	140	6.9	16	20	5390	1930	2300

ROVER

	Engine cc	Power bhp	Fuel	Engine config.	Driven wheels	Top Speed mph	0-60mph secs	MPG average	Insurance group	Length mm	Width mm	Weight kg
Mini												
1.3	1275	63	P	S4	F	92	11.5	43	5	3050	1410	695
200												
211	1113	60	P	S4	F	96	15.0	40	3	3970	1690	950
214	1396	75	P	S4	F	103	12.5	42	4	3970	1690	985
214 16v	1396	103	P	S4	F	115	10.2	40	6	3970	1690	1015
216	1590	111	P	S4	F	118	9.3	39	7	3970	1690	1025
200vi	1795	145	P	S4	F	127	7.5	38	14	3970	1690	1060
220D Turbo	1994	105	D	S4	F	115	9.8	50	5	3970	1690	1105
400												
414	1396	103	P	S4	F	115	11.0	42	9	4490	1700	1120
416	1590	111	P	S4	F	118	10.0	40	11	4490	1700	1125
420	1994	136	P	S4	F	124	9.0	33	13	4490	1700	1265
420 D Turbo	1994	86	D	S4	F	105	13.0	50	10	4490	1700	1240
420 Di Turbo	1994	105	D	S4	F	115	10.4	53	11	4490	1700	1250
Niche												
Cabriolet 1.6	1588	111	P	S4	F	115	9.7	39	11	4216	1680	1100
Tourer 1.6	1588	111	P	S4	F	115	9.7	39	9	4370	1680	1100
Coupe 1.6	1588	111	P	S4	F	121	9.5	39	14	4270	1680	1080
Coupe 1.8	1795	145	P	S4	F	131	7.8	35	15	4270	1680	1090
600												
618	1997	115	P	S4	F	121	10.5	32	10	4650	1720	1275
620	1997	131	P	S4	F	125	9.5	31	11	4650	1720	1290
620ti	1994	197	P	S4	F	143	7.0	30	17	4650	1720	1355
623	2259	158	P	S4	F	134	8.2	29	14	4650	1720	1330
620 TD	1994	104	D	S4	F	115	10.8	50	10	4650	1720	1300
800												
820	1994	136	P	S4	F	125	9.6	32	11	4650	1720	1340
820 Turbo	1994	200	P	S4	F	143	7.3	29	17	4650	1720	1395
825	2497	175	P	V6	F	135	8.2	30	14	4650	1720	1390
825 TD	2498	118	D	S4	F	118	10.5	43	11	4650	1720	1445

MG

	Engine cc	Power bhp	Fuel	Engine config.	Driven wheels	Top Speed mph	0-60mph secs	MPG average	Insurance group	Length mm	Width mm	Weight kg
MGF												
1.8	1795	120	P	S4	R	120	8.5	38	12	3910	1630	1060
1.8 VVC	1795	145	P	S4	R	130	7.0	36	14	3910	1630	1070

SAAB

	Engine cc	Power bhp	Fuel	Engine config.	Driven wheels	Top Speed mph	0-60mph secs	MPG average	Insurance group	Length mm	Width mm	Weight kg
9-3												
2.0	1985	131	P	S4	F	124	11.0	28	10	4629	1711	1295
2.0 Turbo	1985	185	P	S4	F	143	8.5	29	15	4629	1711	1380
2.3	2290	150	P	S4	F	130	10.0	30	14	4629	1711	1320
2.2 TD	2172	116	D	S4	F	124	10.9	42	15	4629	1711	1350
9-5												
2.0 Turbo	1985	147	P	S4	F	135	10.0	29	-	4805	2042	1485
2.3 Turbo	2290	167	P	S4	F	141	8.5	28	-	4805	2042	1500
3.0 Turbo	2962	197	P	V6	F	147	8.0	27	-	4805	2042	1630

SEAT

	Engine cc	Power bhp	Fuel	Engine config.	Driven wheels	Top Speed mph	0-60mph secs	MPG average	Insurance group	Length mm	Width mm	Weight kg
Arosa												
1.0	999	50	P	S4	F	94	17.4	50	2	3536	1639	865
1.4	1390	60	P	S4	F	99	14.1	46	3	3536	1639	895
1.7D	1716	60	D	S4	F	98	16.8	64	3	3536	1639	960